SORCERY!

KHARÉ

CITYPORT OF TRAPS

STEVE JACKSON

SCHOLASTIC

Scholastic Children's Books
An imprint of Scholastic Ltd
Euston House, 24 Eversholt Street, London, NW1 1DB, UK
Registered office: Westfield Road, Southam, Warwickshire, CV47 0RA
SCHOLASTIC and associated logos are trademarks and/or
registered trademarks of Scholastic Inc.

First published in the UK by Penguin Group, 1984
This edition published in the UK by Scholastic Ltd, 2019

Text copyright © Steve Jackson, 1984
Cover and inside illustrations copyright © Steve Jackson, 2019

The right of Steve Jackson to be identified as the Author
of this Work has been asserted in accordance with the
Copyright, Designs and Patents Act 1988

Cover and inside illustrations by Robert Ball, 2019

Fighting Fantasy is a trademark owned by Steve Jackson
and Ian Livingstone, all rights reserved.
Fighting Fantasy Gamebook Concept © Steve
Jackson and Ian Livingstone, 1982

ISBN 978 1407 18848 5

A CIP catalogue record for this book
is available from the British Library.

All rights reserved.
This book is sold subject to the condition that it shall not,
by way of trade or otherwise, be lent, hired out or otherwise circulated in
any form of binding or cover other than that in which it is published. No
part of this publication may be reproduced, stored in a retrieval system,
or transmitted in any form or by any means (electronic, mechanical,
photocopying, recording or otherwise) without prior
written permission of Scholastic Limited.

Printed by CPI Group (UK) Ltd, Croydon, CR0 4YY
Papers used by Scholastic Children's Books are made
from wood grown in sustainable forests.

1 3 5 7 9 10 8 6 4 2

This is a work of fiction. Names, characters, places, incidents
and dialogues are products of the author's imagination or are used
fictitiously. Any resemblance to actual people, living or dead,
events or locales is entirely coincidental.

www.scholastic.co.uk

Official FIGHTING FANTASY website www.fightingfantasy.com

CONTENTS

CONTENTS

INTRODUCTION

Kharé – Cityport of Traps is the second adventure in the *Sorcery!* series, following *The Shamutanti Hills*. But *Sorcery!* has been designed so that each adventure is playable in its own right, whether or not readers have been through the previous ones.

Kharé is, however, a complete adventure within a city. New players will find all the information they need, together with an *Adventure Sheet,* at the end of this book. Readers who are now on the second stage of their journey will be able to skip over the rules section and plunge straight into the adventure: their characters, equipment and experience must be carried over from the previous adventure.

THE SIMPLE AND ADVANCED GAMES

Beginners may wish to start with the simple game, ignoring the use of magic. Rules for fighting creatures with swords and other weapons are given in each adventure book, using a combat system similar to that used in *The*

Warlock of Firetop Mountain, the original Fighting Fantasy Gamebook. By rolling dice, you battle creatures with weapons only.

More experienced players will wish to progress quickly on to the advanced game, in which your fighting ability is somewhat limited but your most powerful weapon will be your knowledge of magic, a much more powerful tool. In actual fact, the advanced game is fairly simple to learn. There is no reason why beginners should not proceed with the use of magic from the start. But learning spells will take some time and practice with the *Spell Book,* and the 'simple' option is given for players who wish to start their adventure with minimum delay.

HOW WILL YOU START
YOUR ADVENTURE?

The book you hold in your hands is a gateway to another world – a world of dark magic, terrifying monsters, brooding castles, treacherous dungeons and untold danger, where a noble few defend against the myriad schemes of the forces of evil. Welcome to the world of **FIGHTING FANTASY!**

You are about to embark upon a thrilling fantasy adventure in which **YOU** are the hero! **YOU** decide which route to take, which dangers to risk and which creatures to fight. But be warned – it will also be **YOU** who has to live or die by the consequences of your actions.

Take heed, for success is by no means certain, and you may well fail in your mission on your first attempt. But

9

have no fear, for with experience, skill and luck, each new attempt should bring you a step closer to your ultimate goal.

Prepare yourself, for when you turn the page you will enter an exciting, perilous **FIGHTING FANTASY** adventure where every choice is yours to make, an adventure in which **YOU ARE THE HERO!**

How would you like to begin your adventure?

IF YOU ARE NEW TO FIGHTING FANTASY ...

It's a good idea to read through the rules which appear on pages 261-275 before you start.

IF YOU HAVE PLAYED FIGHTING FANTASY BEFORE ...

You'll realize that to have any chance of success, you will need to discover your hero's attributes. You can create your own character by following the instructions on pages 261-262. Don't forget to enter your character's details on the Adventure Sheet which appears on page 296.

If you wish to play the advanced game, be sure to read the rules on pages 267-275 on how to use magic.

ALTERNATIVE DICE

If you do not have a pair of dice handy, dice rolls are printed throughout the book at the bottom of the pages. Flicking rapidly through the book and stopping on a page will give you a random dice roll, If you need to 'roll' only one die, read only the first printed die; if two, total the two dice symbols.

THE LEGEND OF
THE CROWN OF KINGS

Centuries ago, in the time we now call the Dark Ages, whole regions of the world were undiscovered. There were pockets of civilization, each with their own races and cultures. One such region was Kakhabad, a dark land at the end of the earth.

Although several warlords had tried, Kakhabad had never been ruled. All manner of evil creatures, forced from the more civilized lands beyond the Zanzunu Peaks, had gradually crawled into Kakhabad, which became known as the Verminpit at Earthend.

Civilization and order had spread throughout the rest of the known world ever since the discovery of the Crown of Kings by Chalanna the Reformer, of Femphrey. With its help, Chalanna became Emperor of the largest empire in the eastern world. This magical Crown had mysterious powers, bestowing supernormal qualities of leadership and justice on its owner. But Chalanna's own ambitions were not of conquest. He wished instead to establish peaceful nation-states, aligned to Femphrey. Thus in his wisdom he passed the fabled Crown from ruler to ruler in the neighbouring kingdoms, and, with the help of its magical powers, one by one these lands became peaceful and prosperous.

The path was set. Each ruler would own the Crown of Kings for a four-year period in which to establish order within his kingdom and fall in with the growing Femphrey Alliance. So far the kingdoms of Ruddlestone, Lendleland, Gallantaria and Brice had taken their turns under the rule of the Crown. The benefits were immediate. War and strife were virtually unknown.

The King of Analand duly received the Crown of Kings amid great ceremony, and, from that day onwards, the development of Analand was ensured. No one quite knew how the Crown of Kings could have such an enormous uplifting effect on a whole nation. Some said it was divinely inspired; some that its power was merely in the mind. But one thing was certain – its effects were unquestionable. All was well in Analand, until the night of the Black Moon.

The King was the first to discover that the Crown was missing. Carried off on that starless night by Birdmen from Xamen, the Crown was on its way to Mampang in the outlaw territories of Kakhabad. News came from the Baklands that the Crown was being carried to the Archmage of Mampang whose ambitions were to make Kakhabad his kingdom.

Although Kakhabad was a dangerous land, it was in itself little threat to the surrounding kingdoms. The lack of rule meant it had no army and its own internal struggles kept it permanently preoccupied. But with the Crown of Kings to establish rule, Kakhabad could potentially be a deadly enemy to all members of the Femphrey Alliance.

Such was the shame that fell on Analand for the loss of the Crown that all benefits from two years under its rule soon disappeared. Law, order and morale were breaking down. The King was losing the confidence of his subjects. Neighbouring territories were looking suspiciously across their borders. There were even whisperings of invasions.

One hope remained. Someone – for a military force would never survive the journey – must travel to Mampang and rescue the Crown of Kings. Only on its safe return would the dreadful curse be lifted from Analand. You have volunteered yourself for this quest and your mission is clear. You must cross Kakhabad to the Mampang Fortress and find the Crown!

YOUR
ADVENTURE
AWAITS!

MAY YOUR STAMINA NEVER FAIL!

NOW TURN OVER...

1

Kharé: the city of chaos – and gateway to the Baklands.

Below you, at the foot of the Shamutanti Hills, sprawls the walled cityport, slashed viciously by the great Jabaji River. Halfway down the hills, you pause to survey your destination. Legend has it that Kharé arose around the only ford across the Jabaji between Lake Lumle and the sea. But this is an unlikely tale. More probable are the stories of river pirates camping in the area, waiting to ambush the small sailing vessels which carried their cargoes of fish between Lake Lumlé and the Kakhabad Sea. Whatever the reasons, Kharé grew.

As the camp became a village, and the village a city, Kharé became a magnet for the ne'er-do-wells of the Baklands and the Shamutantis. A multitude of malevolent creatures who would kill you for the laces from your boots drifted into the city. Their lawlessness gave rise to an elaborate system of traps devised by the inhabitants to protect themselves from the criminals who roamed the streets. This is how the city got its name: Cityport of Traps.

Your own goal lies well beyond Kharé which, knowing only its reputation, you would prefer not to pass through. But pass through you must, for elsewhere crossing the Jabaji is impossible. From your vantage point you can trace the fortified wall which surrounds the cityport. Two gates open Kharé to the rest of the world. Before you is the South Gate, your only way in. And on the far side of the city is the North Gate, leading on to the Baklands.

Time is passing, and time is precious. You stride off downhill at a brisk pace, and reach the gate within the hour. It is locked. If you have a large key, presented to you by the Svinn chief, you may turn to the reference given when you received this gift. If you do not have the key, you may either knock loudly for the guards (turn to **178**) or cast a spell:

BAM	BIG	HUF	DOP	HOT
337	**496**	**408**	**381**	**474**

2

Where will you kiss next: the forehead (turn to **314**); the left eye (turn to **163**); the right cheek (turn to **334**); the left cheek (turn to **88**); the nose (turn to **296**); or the lips (turn to **231**)?

3

Two artisans look particularly interesting: an artist with no hands who is exhibiting a series of portraits and a firemaster who is displaying ornate fires, all coloured in different hues. Which do you want to look at: the artist's works (turn to **18**) or the firemaster's fires (turn to **96**)?

4

The great bronze foot descends on to you. You try to spring out of the way ... but too late. It crushes you into the ground. Your journey has ended here.

5

A pouch drops out of the cabinet to the ground by your feet. You open it and look inside, but it seems to be empty. You may take it with you, perhaps to hold gold if your own pouch is lost. You will soon discover that the pouch was not empty at all. As you opened it, a family of fleas sprang on to your arms and is now making itself a home around your body. But you will not notice this until their bites start itching some time later. Apart from the inconvenience, though, they are no real problem. You leave the tent and continue. Turn to **160**.

6

The stallion bucks and leaps as it carries you off down the road. You try desperately to hold on but without success: it throws you through the air to land in a verge. Deduct 2 *STAMINA* points for landing awkwardly on your shoulder. You pick yourself up and dust yourself off. The horse disappears around the bend ahead and you can make your way back towards the fork. Turn to **237**.

7

What will you take from your pack? Do you have any of the following: a black mask; a bow and arrows; a magical chain? If so, choose one of them, note that you are carrying it, and enter the crypt. Turn to **249**.

8

You walk up to the statue, thinking it must be the work of an artist of great talent, as it looks very realistic. But then the 'statue' blinks, giving the game away; but your reactions will not be swift enough.

In a flash the creature's long arms shoot out towards you, clamp themselves on to your shoulders, and recoil, lifting you into the air and up to its face. It opens its jaws and sinks sharp teeth into your neck. You are dead before you realize what has happened! You have discovered one of Kharé's most deadly inhabitants – the MANTIS MAN.

9

Opposite the Chainmaker's hut is another, from which a pleasant smell is wafting. You may go over and see what's happening if you like (turn to **171**). Otherwise you may continue down the road (turn to **294**)

10

You find yourself in a dead-end passage. You will have to turn round and take another route. Which way will you go?

Continue straight as far as possible?   Turn to **298**
Second right and continue as far as possible?   Turn to **174**
First right and continue as far as possible?   Turn to **69**

The Living Corpse reels from its power

Your blow lands squarely in the chest of the foul, undead creature. The Living Corpse reels from its power, but though the blow would have felled any mortal being, it does not kill the monstrosity; instead it breaks its body up into six components and all six now surround you, clawing, biting, kicking and shoving. Your battle is now against a head, a torso, two arms and two legs, all of which are attacking you at the same time.

If you will continue to fight with your weapon, you will hack at the bits of body, whose scores are:

Roll	Part	SKILL	STAMINA
1	Head	3	1
2	Torso	2	1
3	Left Arm	3	1
4	Right Arm	3	1
5	Left Leg	2	1
6	Right Leg	2	1

Treat each part of the corpse's body as a separate opponent and roll to determine its Attack Strength. Then roll your own Attack Strength. Any part of the body which has a higher Attack Strength than you inflicts one hit. For your own attack, roll one die to determine which part of the body you will fight: your blow is aimed at the body part rolled (see the table above). If your Attack Strength is higher than that of the body part, you have put it out of action and it will not roll for its Attack Strength in subsequent rounds – but it will remain in the battle (so if you roll the same number again you have wasted the blow). If you defeat the creature, turn to **276**.

You may, if you wish, cast a spell rather than fight:

POP	WOK	WAL	SIX	RES
441	**450**	**373**	**435**	**357**

12

Taking the key from your pack, you carefully insert it into the lock. One by one the tumblers click. The door gives a little and you ease it open, peering cautiously inside. There is no one about.

You slip quickly inside and close the gate behind you. *Damn!* You have left the key in the lock outside (cross this off your *Adventure Sheet*). You tiptoe into the archway which covers the gate and hide in an alcove. There is no sound and you decide to venture out into the open. Your first cover is a building just inside the wall and you nip over to it. It is made of stone and the windows are barred. Looking inside you can see that the room is bare apart from a wooden bench, on which an old man is sitting. Will you enter the building and greet the man (turn to **169**) or leave and continue onwards (turn to **218**)?

13

He fires the arrow as you attack. Will it strike its mark? Throw one die to see where it hits:

1. It pierces your eye. You die instantly
2. It hits you in the chest: Lose 5 *STAMINA* points
3. It sinks into your leg. Lose 3 *STAMINA* points
4. It ricks your arm. Lose 2 *STAMINA* points
5. It cuts the wrist on your sword arm. Lose 1 *STAMINA* point and deduct 2 *SKILL* points
6. It misses

If you are still alive, resolve your battle:

MURDERER   *SKILL* 7   *STAMINA* 8

If you win, turn to **105**.

14

The man has seen how the fight is going. When you defeat the Bristle Beast, he slams the door shut. You try opening it but it is locked tight and you will not be able to enter. Turn to **133**.

15

The guillotine blade rises and you breathe a sigh of relief. The innkeeper curses and disappears downstairs, allowing you to release your bonds. You leave the inn smartly. Add 1 *LUCK* point for the correct choice. Turn to **267**. You may add 2 *STAMINA* points for your night's sleep.

16

You leave the crypt, carefully avoiding the shimmering circle by the door, and head off down the road out of Kharé. Turn to **127**.

17

You try your best to follow the steps of the dancers, but without too much success. Nevertheless, you are enjoying yourself and may add 1 *STAMINA* point. But the dance begins to tire you, particularly as you are still carrying your backpack and weapon. The tune seems nowhere near ending. Will you last to the end of the tune? Count the number of artefacts you are carrying (include your weapon, your Provisions and your Gold as three artefacts) and throw two dice. If the number you roll is *higher than* that number, then you last out until the end of the dance without becoming over-exhausted. If you roll a number *less than* or *equal to* the number of artefacts you have, you must lose 1 *STAMINA* point and roll again, repeating this procedure until you roll higher than your artefacts. The more you are carrying, the more exhausted you will become. If you roll unsuccessfully five times, you collapse to the ground and get pulled back to the edge of the dance by the crowd. Turn next to **201**.

18

The artist's portraits are of various nobles in Kharé. You wonder how he can possibly paint without hands and he explains that he has a magical paintbrush with which he can paint by will. He tells you that he is now actually using the paintbrush to paint inside his hut. Do you want to enter the hut to see his current creation (turn to **176**) or will you look instead at the firemaster's fires (turn to **96**)?

19

You brush against one particularly noisy chain and the sound brings the Chainmaker in through the other door. You recognize him as a SVINN, a man-orc from the village of Torrepani, and he is outraged at your intrusion. Turn to **119**.

20

The talisman is quite a find. While wearing this and *Testing your Luck,* you need not deduct a *LUCK* point if you are Unlucky. Return to **264**.

21

Gain 2 *STAMINA* points for your rest. You awake at sunrise the next morning. Did you eat at all yesterday? If not you must deduct 3 *STAMINA* points as you are now very hungry.

As you wake, you hear a sound at the door. The guards have returned. Presumably they are satisfied that you are no threat to the city and they shove you outside, followed by the old man. In something of a daze, you both stumble off down the road into Kharé, he a little ahead of you. You watch him and are reminded of your suspicions. You stop and check your pack. You should not have trusted the blackguard as he has stolen an artefact from you! Cross one item (of your choice) off your *Adventure Sheet* (if you have no artefacts, you must lose 1 item from your Provisions). You shout after him but he is some way ahead by now and has turned right at a junction. You will have to run to catch up. Turn to **81**.

22

Which spell will you try?

MUD	SIX	RAN	LAW	YOB
358	**384**	**454**	**491**	**411**

If you know none of these, you must fight the Statue (turn to **299**).

23

You follow the children up the road. Homes and hovels line the track and you are wary as you pass. Strange faces appear at the windows, watching you. From around the bend ahead, a troop of guards appears! Thinking swiftly, you dart into a hut by the roadside and close the door. The guards march past and you breathe a sigh of relief. But where are you?

You look around the dismal hut and jump as you see three ugly faces gawping at you! The room is untidy and contains little more than a straw mattress and a low table. The three creatures, a group of BLACK ELVES, are staring vacantly at you. A heavy, sweet smell hits your nostrils and explains their lethargy. They are puffing at a hookah containing Smoking Weed. One of them gathers himself together enough to talk to you and asks you to join them. What will you do?

Sit down with them and draw on the hookah?	Turn to **150**
Apologize for disturbing them and leave?	Turn to **213**
See if you can learn any information from them?	Turn to **242**
Draw your weapon and challenge them?	Turn to **58**

24

They move towards you and you nip down a side street to the left. They chase after you. They are quick runners and you will have to try to lose them. Will you turn:

First right, first left, first right?	Turn to **232**
First right, next right, first left?	Turn to **41**
First left, first right, next right?	Turn to **184**

Or cast a spell:

JIG	ROK	YOB	NIF	YAZ
489	**458**	**354**	**407**	**510**

25

The Wheel of Fortune will cost you 1 Gold Piece per spin. To play this game, pay your Gold Piece, remember this reference (so you may return afterwards) and close the book. On some pages of the book, next to the printed dice, details of winnings are given. Flick through the book and open it at random. If no winning message appears, you lose. If a winning message appears, you win that number of Gold Pieces (5, 10 or 20). You may pay and play as often as you like until you win. When you win, you must leave the hall (turn to **39**).

26

Which spell will you use?

RAP	ZIP	YAG	DUD	HUF
483	**439**	**428**	**475**	**465**

If you know none of these, you will have to offer them a bribe (turn to **157**), otherwise they will move you on.

27

Inside the hut, bones litter the floor. Whoever, or whatever, lives here is evidently carnivorous. Judging by the size of some of the bones, this creature seems to be quite partial to humans. As the hut is otherwise deserted, you search through the rubble. The unfortunate victims' clothes are strewn about, and in the pockets you find 15 Gold Pieces. You also find a number of knuckle bones which have been strung together into a bracelet. You may take this and the Gold Pieces with you. Cautiously you leave the hut, after first making sure that no one is about. Turn to **37**.

28

Further up the road, you reach a fork where you may continue either straight ahead or up to the left. A hut stands in the fork and a stallion is tied up outside it. You may take the track up to the left (turn to **300**), continue ahead (turn to **233**) or you may walk over to the horse (turn to **183**).

29

You open the box and look inside. It seems to contain all the creature's valuable possessions, few as they are. An elaborately carved mirror with a gold back is the most impressive item. The parchment scroll contains writings in a language which you do not understand, but you may take it with you anyway. 2 Gold Pieces are also lying in the box. You leave the hut quickly. Turn to **294**.

30

You pray to your deity. You hear a small click from the door and the Elvin whispers, 'Psst! It's worked! The door is open!' You may now leave whenever you wish, but you decide to wait until the guard has fallen asleep. You make a silent prayer of thanks to Libra – but remember that you may not call on her help again in this adventure. Turn to **206**.

31

You bend down to the idol's lips as the god gives its answer: 'The spell is known only by Sansas, First Noble of Kharé. But such knowledge will be of little use as Sansas is not in the city. He is sailing up the Jabaji towards Lake Lumle.' You curse: your question has been useless, and was not the one to ask. You must now leave the Shrine of Courga and head for the North Gate. Turn to **109**.

A great bald-headed brute steps into the ring

32

You follow the track up past the huts until you reach a junction where you turn right. Turn to **297**.

33

From within the ropes of the ring, the ruffian's voice is announcing the challenger: 'All right, folks, we now have a challenger. In the white corner, let's hear your appreciation for Anvar the Barbarian!' Cheers come from the onlookers. 'And in the black corner, brawling champion of Kharé: the mighty Ogre, the one they call Skullsplitter-Cagou of Daddu-Ley!' Again, cheers come from the crowd as a great bald-headed brute steps into the ring. This should be quite a fight. The Barbarian is taller than the Ogre, but the Ogre's arms and legs are solid muscle. Wagers are being made in the crowd. You may, if you wish, bet on the outcome of the fight (turn to **190**) or you may decide just to watch. You may wish to take up the champion's challenge yourself, as the prize for the winner is 15 Gold Pieces. Turn to **234** if you do not wish to bet.

WIN 5 GOLD PIECES

34

He returns with two mugs of ale, deliberately placing one in front of you. 'The centre of Kharé is around the port,' he says, 'and it is a dangerous place to be at night. Many street wanderers get waylaid and captured for the slave ships, so make sure you are settled in an inn before sundown. And another thing ... but come, drink your ale.' You have not yet started your drink. Will you sup and let him continue (turn to **236**) or will you cast a spell?

HOP	FAR	TEL	SUS	RAN
361	**387**	**498**	**414**	**355**

35

The smooth metal has no obvious weak spots. While you are trying to find one, the creature's great foot kicks at you and catches you in the side. Lose 4 *STAMINA* points. Return to **326** and choose again.

36

You look towards the guard on the gate who taunts you with a mocking smile. You have been tricked! You may try to cause trouble by exposing him as a cheat (turn to **126**) or you may decide you had better keep quiet and cooperate (turn to **291**).

37

As you leave the hut, you glance once more at the statue. Although you are not sure, you have the feeling that something has changed. Then it dawns on you that something *has* changed. Its head has moved round and is now pointing towards you! Will you run swiftly away (turn to **55**), draw your weapon (turn to **76**), or cast a spell?

HOW	TEL	FIX	LAW	ROK
492	**401**	**394**	**461**	**348**

38

Deathwraiths may only be harmed by silver weapons. If you have the bow with silver-tipped arrows, you may pull these out of your pack and turn to **147**. If you do not have the bow and arrows, your only hope is to pray to Libra if you have not yet used her help in this adventure (turn to **87**). Otherwise this will be your last fight in Kharé . . .

39

On the way out of the Gambling Halls, you pass a door marked 'Portal Room'. If you wish to investigate, turn to **112**. If you'd rather just leave, turn to **197**. If you now have more Gold than you came in with, you may add 2 *LUCK* points.

40

The creatures in the crowd around you become angry at your refusal to join in. They push you forward and you try to hold yourself back. 'Where's your spirit?' challenges one voice behind you, while another snarls: 'G'waan. It's only a bit of fun.' Will you still insist on declining the invitation to dance (turn to **230**) or decide not to risk angering the crowd (turn to **17**)?

41

You come to a stop outside a hut. The footsteps behind you are getting louder. You decide to nip into the hut. Turn to **324**.

42

You are in a dead-end passage. You must turn round and head back. Which way will you go?

Straight ahead, second right, first left?   Turn to **10**

Straight ahead, first right, second left, first right?   Turn to **77**

Straight ahead, first left?   Turn to **174**

43

You look around the room. Herbs, vegetables and meats are lying on tables around the centre of the room and hanging from the walls. Evidently you are in a kitchen of some kind. At the far end of the room is a fire in a chimney and suspended over the fire is a pot containing a bubbling broth, the source of the smell which you picked up out in the road. Standing by the fire is an odd-looking creature. It has a humanoid torso and legs but its head is a solid blob of jelly and its eyes float loosely about in the 'front' of its face. Hanging down from its head on all sides are numerous long tentacles. These appear to be its hands (as it has no others) and it grips a ladle and stirring spoon. This strange creature holds your attention, but under one of the tables you have noticed a box, from which a scroll and a shiny mirror protrude. Your host is waiting for your reaction. Will you:

Try to talk to it?   Turn to **145**

Draw your weapon and attack?   Turn to **243**

Cast a spell?   Turn to **257**

Leave and continue on your way?   Turn to **294**

44

You try to grab the paintbrush but it twists and squirms out of your grip, darting back to the painting at every opportunity. You may draw your weapon and duel with it:

PAINTBRUSH SKILL 8 STAMINA 5

The brush will not actually attack you: its *SKILL* merely reflects its ability to dodge. If you do not break it (i.e. kill it) by the fifth Attack Round, it manages to finish the painting. Turn to **67**. If you do break it, you may now leave the hut (turn to **137**).

45

The bag contains 6 teeth from Dark Goblins. You pour them into your hand and to your delight there is an added bonus. A large Giant's tooth, which the Gnome did not know was there, is at the bottom of the bag. Return to **264**.

46

Continuing along the streets, you reach another junction, where you may either turn left (turn to **131**), right (turn to **60**), or carry straight on (turn to **139**).

47

You enter the graveyard and walk along an overgrown path up to the door of the crypt. On the ground before the door is a shimmering circle of darkness which you will have to cross or jump over to get to the doorway. Will you walk up to the door (turn to **288**), jump over the circle (turn to **258**), or cast a spell?

ZIP	SUS	DOC	HOW	TEL
466	**377**	**442**	**395**	**418**

48

The priest cannot hide his disappointment. Apparently the people of Kharé are not trained in the science of mathematics, as you were in Analand. As he has agreed, he will grant you one wish. You ask him what he knows of the spell to open the North Gate of Kharé. 'I am unable to tell you the spell in its entirety,' he says, 'as only the First Noble of Kharé knows all four lines. But I can tell you one line, which is: "I bid you, portals, open wide."' His audience is amazed at your wisdom and they shout out their good wishes as you leave the chapel. Restore your *LUCK* score to its *Initial* level. Now turn to **165**.

49

You release its reins and swing yourself up on to its back. It whinnies loudly and rears up into the air. Before you can react, it bolts off back down the road the way you came. You may hold on tightly and see where it takes you (turn to **268**) or *Test your Luck* in an attempt to stop it and get off (turn to **220**).

50

You creep round the edge of the square, keeping your eyes fixed on the monument. As you pass one doorway, hands grab your arms and neck. 'Looks like we have an intruder!' says a voice. 'We Red-Eyes don't like intruders. Off to the gaol with you!' They bundle you off down the side streets until you reach a large square building. You are taken inside and locked in a cell. Turn to **143**.

51

'Let's see,' he ponders. 'Who may know a line of the North Gate spell? Ah, yes. At the junction ahead, do not *not* carry straight on. Eventually, do not take a left turn. Yes … I think that's it. Good luck!' You are not quite sure what he has actually advised you to do and you consider his advice as you approach the crossroads. Remember he is a compulsive liar! Turn to **144**.

52

Where will you kiss next: the right eye (turn to **2**); the left eye (turn to **163**); the right cheek (turn to **334**); the left cheek (turn to **88**); the nose (turn to **296**); or the lips (turn to **141**)?

53

He calms down and admits that his hearing is not as sharp as it used to be. He is naturally suspicious of strangers in a place such as this. He begins to invite you in but then sees your weapon. If you wish to enter, you will have to hand him your weapon (turn to **229**). Otherwise he will not allow you in and you must leave (turn to **133**).

WIN 10 GOLD PIECES

54

You pick up the hideous creature, carry it over to the coffin and dump it inside. You are exhausted from the battle and rest for a few moments. If you would like to eat Provisions, you may do so, adding 2 *STAMINA* points if you have not yet eaten today (1 *STAMINA* point if you have eaten already). Turn to **209**.

55

As you move, the statue springs! Landing close to you, its hands shoot out and try to grab you. This creature is a deadly MANTIS MAN. If it catches you in its hands, it will draw you in and its sharp teeth will kill you instantly. However, you may attack its arms and, if you disable it, it will be helpless.

MANTIS MAN   *SKILL 6*   *STAMINA 5*

Its form of attack is to fling its arms out at you. At the

start of each Attack Round, roll 2 dice before combat. If you roll a number *less than* the Mantis Man's *SKILL*, it has grabbed you and you have no hope of survival. If the number is *equal to or higher than its SKILL*, it has missed – roll again for Attack Strength as normal. If you survive, turn to **117**.

56

You enter the hall. In spite of the time of day, a noisy crowd is inside. No one notices your entry as everyone is preoccupied with their games. The click of dice and the clatter of the Wheel of Fortune are the only sounds that can be heard above the hubbub. Do you wish to try your luck with the Wheel of Fortune (turn to **25**), on the dice table (turn to **188**), or will you leave the Gambling Halls of Vlada (turn to **39**)?

57

The road leads onwards. You are nearing the centre of Kharé, and the homes and buildings are more densely located. As you are walking along one side of the road and watching the other, you are grabbed from behind and pulled into a building! You spin to face your attacker. He is a dark-skinned man with a stubbly beard. He is evidently surprised at your strength and releases you, holding up his hands to show that he means no harm. 'My friend, I am very sorry for giving you a fright,' he says. 'But I am a lonely man in this city of evil. You are a human like myself and I have not seen you in these parts before. Pray sit down with me and talk for awhile. I'll do you no harm.' He seems friendly enough, but there is a mischievous glint in his eye that you do not trust. You are in his home, which is furnished with a table, chairs and cupboards of wood, and woven tapestries hanging on the walls. Will you stay and talk with him (turn to **186**) or do you wish to leave (turn to **173**)?

58

The others stagger to their feet and grope clumsily at their weapons. Resolve your fight with them (fight them one at a time):

	SKILL	STAMINA
First BLACK ELF	6	5
Second BLACK ELF	7	4
Third BLACK ELF	5	5

Smoking Weed makes co-ordination difficult. Each time a wound is struck by anyone who has indulged (including you), roll one die. If an even number is rolled, the hit is successful. If an odd number is rolled, the blow misses. If a 1 is rolled, the blow misses and the striker stumbles on to his own weapon, causing 2 *STAMINA* points of self-inflicted damage. If you defeat the creatures, turn to **251**.

59

He smiles slyly, looks over his shoulder to check he is not being watched and holds his hand out to you. You drop the coins into his palm (deduct 2 Gold Pieces). As they clink he coughs loudly to cover up the sound. With a whisper he tells you to wait a second. He closes the door on you. Turn to **225**.

60

The street eventually meets another. Turning left will take you into the centre of Kharé and you take this route. Turn to **165**.

61

A short distance ahead is a large house made of stones and mortar. It looks quite an important place. Do you wish to walk up to the front door (turn to **140**), creep round the back (turn to **208**), or walk past it further down the road (turn to **133**)?

62

A little way further along, you reach a sort of crossroads where a track crosses your road. To the left it runs up to another group of huts, while to the right it heads towards what seems to be a fair of some sort where coloured flags are waving and there is plenty of activity. Will you go left (turn to **32**), right (turn to **322**), or straight ahead (turn to **57**)?

63

With great relief, you find that your own Gold is still safe within its pouch. Scuffles are breaking out in the crowd as the pickpocket's victims are challenging their neighbours. You decide to leave. Will you make your way over to the dance (turn to **261**), head for the ring to see whether the champion has any challengers (turn to **33**), or leave the festival (turn to **263**)?

64

You leap out of the way just in time as the great foot descends towards you. But you land awkwardly on your weapon arm. You must deduct 1 *SKILL* point for the rest of this day (your arm will have recovered tomorrow). Turn to **93** and choose again.

65

The shiny surface appears to be a pool of shimmering black liquid. As you peer into it, footsteps come up behind you. 'So a stranger wonders about our Portals, eh?' cackles a voice. 'Well, that's where we dump our rubbish – and any unwanted strangers!' Before you can turn round, two hands shove you into the circle. Turn to **270**.

66

You walk up to the door. A name-plate in the middle reads CHAINMAKER. The door is ajar and you enter. No one is inside, but another door is open to the back of the hut. The room you are standing in is draped in chains of all lengths and strengths and you can barely move round without touching them. Will you call out for the Chainmaker (turn to **280**) or have a quick look around the room while no one is about (turn to **215**)?

67

As the painting is completed, to your astonishment the image *moves* on its canvas. Looking directly at you, the painting moves its hands to grab the edges of the canvas, hauls itself off the board, and climbs down on to the ground. Before you stands a duplicate of yourself! You look at each other for a moment. A voice comes from outside and the artist commands the painting to attack you and grab your money. Resolve your combat with your double (it has the same *SKILL* and *STAMINA* as you have). If you win, you may leave the hut (turn to **137**). Alternatively, you may cast a spell. As the artist did not realize you were a sorcerer, he has endowed his creation with no magical powers:

DUD	SAP	ZEN	SUD	RAZ
356	**385**	**508**	**364**	**339**

68

You leave the inn and wander round the streets, trying to find a suitable place to rest for the night. Would you like to choose a dark alley behind the inn to sleep (turn to **94**) or will you stay awake all night (turn to **159**)?

69

You arrive in a dead-end passageway. But a light is shining into the passage from above. You look up and can see a hole in the top of the sewer – and a rope is hanging down with a bucket on the end of it! Perhaps you have found a disused well!

You leap up and grab the rope. You start your long shinny up the rope to the light above. This is a tiring climb and you must lose 2 *STAMINA* points; but you can add 2 *LUCK* points for finding a way out of the sewers. At the top you find you are indeed returning to the surface through a well. You rest to catch your breath and then you may either continue ahead out of Kharé (turn to **319**) or back towards the cityport to investigate a building standing in a graveyard (turn to **83**).

70

You mouth a silent prayer to Libra. You feel no different, but she is with you in the battle that will take place. Your first successful attack on the champion will kill him instantly. Turn to **323** and resolve the battle. But remember that you have now used your one and only opportunity for help from your goddess in Kharé. You may not choose an option to pray to her again until you have left the cityport.

71

A small bracelet drops out of the cabinet. You pick it up and turn it over. It is made from the finger-bones of a dwarf and it may be useful for your spells. You put it in your pack and leave the tent. Turn to **160**.

72

He bends over to look at your choice. 'You jest!' he cries. 'The answer is most certainly not that rune. Stranger, if such is your wisdom, you will need more than the help of your goddess on this journey.' He wishes to continue with his work and you must leave his house. You collect your sword on the way out. Turn to **133**.

73

You try the door at the entrance and it swings open, creaking on its hinges. This sound is amplified by the hollow temple inside and it echoes eerily for several moments. Cautiously, you peer inside. The place seems to be deserted; you can hear no signs of activity. Stepping into the shrine and closing the door behind you, the sight that greets your eyes takes your breath away.

The walls are decorated with brightly coloured murals depicting scenes from the religious mythology of Kharé. Fine ornaments in precious metals are set in alcoves around the pews, and rich, woven tapestries cover every surface. A cunning trick of architecture catches the wind and an ethereal humming is a constant background noise. Four large stone gargoyles of winged demons watch over the shrine from their mounts high in the eaves and at the far end of the room is the focal point of the temple: the altar.

Steps leading up to the altar seems to have been designed to emphasize the centrepiece of the shrine – a large golden idol fashioned in Courga's image.

Will you make sure there is no one about (turn to **168**), check the shrine for traps (turn to **224**), see if you can find anything precious worth stealing (turn to **205**), or investigate the idol (turn to **122**)? Alternatively you may cast a spell:

MAG	DOC	WOK	SUS	TEL
431	**485**	**374**	**503**	**477**

74

Is the beggar still alive? If so, turn to **207**. If he is not, you can continue on your journey after a short rest – turn to **148**.

75

You shove open the door and step forwards, your hand ready with your weapon. But a small vial of liquid was balanced on top of the door and has now landed on your head, spilling its contents. You reach up and rub your head. An oily liquid is matting your hair. When you look at your hand, it is covered in hair! Again you feel your head and this time you pull off a great tuft of hair. 'Serves you right, intruder,' gloats a voice from within the hut. 'Perhaps baldness will teach you some manners!' You reach up again to rub your head and with a shock your hand strokes a bald scalp! In fact the effects of this Potion of Baldness are only temporary. Once you have washed your head, the hair will grow again – but it will be some time before your full head of hair is restored! Turn to **43**.

76

You draw your weapon and, as you move, the statue springs to life! It lands before you on its spindly legs with its hands and arms still fixed in a praying position. With lightning speed its arms shoot forwards to try and grab you. This creature is a deadly MANTIS MAN and you must fight it:

MANTIS MAN   *SKILL 6*   *STAMINA 5*

The Mantis Man uses its whiplash-like arms in attack. It will try to catch you and draw you into its mouth, where sharp teeth will guarantee instant death. At the start of each Attack Round, throw two dice for the creature. If the number rolled is *less than* its *SKILL*, it has caught you and death is certain. If you roll *equal to* or *higher than* its *SKILL*, it has missed – roll for Attack Strength as normal. Your only hope is to attack its arms, for if you can injure an arm, it will be unable to attack (hence its low *STAMINA*). If you survive, turn to **117**.

A shape rises out of the water

77

You arrive in a dead-end passage, knee deep in sewage. A bubbling in the liquid ahead of you makes you apprehensive and, as you watch, a shape rises out of the water. The smooth, flabby shape of a large SLIME EATER stands before you. It sees you and roars loudly, reaching out at you with its blubbery arms. You will have to fight the creature:

SLIME EATER   SKILL 7   STAMINA 11

If you defeat it, turn to **196**. You may prefer to fight with magic:

GOB	JIG	TEL	YAP	DOZ
471	**427**	**488**	**479**	**393**

78

Where will you kiss next: the forehead (turn to **52**); the left eye (turn to **163**); the right cheek (turn to **334**); the left cheek (turn to **88**); the nose (turn to **296**); or the lips (turn to **231**)?

WIN 5 GOLD PIECES

79

Flanker, the assassin you met near Torrepani, arrived in Kharé a day ahead of you. If you arrive at either of the references listed below, you may bump into him and talk with him. Memorize these references (you may not write them down: this is, if you like, equivalent to whether or not you recognize him). If you arrive at either of these references, turn to the corresponding follow-up reference to see what Flanker says.

If you arrive at **244**   Turn to **111**
If you arrive at **110**   Turn to **222**

80

They scoff at your meagre offering. 'Are we being offered a bribe, brothers, or is this traveller merely tossing us a beggar's alms?' asks the leader. He snatches your three coins and flips one each to the other two. 'If we are to look the other way for you,' he snarls, 'you had better make it worth our while. Give us another 5 Gold Pieces each!' If you pay up, turn to **113**. Otherwise you may only continue if you can use your magic to trick them. Turn to **26**.

81

You reach the junction ahead. This offers you three ways on. You are on the outskirts of the city and huts are grouped loosely about the tracks leading into the cityport

To the left a group of scruffy youngsters are walking away up the roadway with packs on their backs. Ahead, the road leads straight into the centre of Kharé and would appear to be the main road. To the right, you see the old man disappearing into a hut on the left-hand side of the track. Which direction will you choose:

Turn left?	Turn to **23**
Continue straight ahead?	Turn to **138**
Turn right?	Turn to **292**

82

Your challenge is accepted. The crowd cheers you as you step into the white corner. You feel confident that you will be able to defeat the champion now he has been weakened in his last fight. But as you look over at him in the black corner, your heart sinks: trickery is afoot. The ruffian secretly casts a healing spell over his man, restoring him to full strength! You may use your own magic to help you:

DOC	VIK	GAK	YOB	GOD
405	**362**	**497**	**451**	**425**

Or you may call on help from Libra (turn to **70**). If you wish to do neither of these, the fight will start – turn to **323**.

83

Further up the road, you pass a small graveyard overhung with leafy branches. Gravestones are scattered in no particular order around an old crypt which stands in the centre. A sign above the doorway to the crypt reads: HERE RESTS LORD SHINVA – FIFTH NOBLE OF KHARÉ. Do you wish to enter the crypt (turn to **47**) or do you think it would be safer to head out of the cityport (turn to **127**)?

84

You soon arrive at another crossroads where you may either turn left (turn to **57**) or carry straight on (turn to **322**).

85

If you wish to grab the coin, you must *Test your Luck* (if you do not wish to waste your *LUCK*, leave the pond by turning to **28**). The little silverfish will be outraged if you try to take its coin and will dart out and bite you. If you are Lucky, you manage to grab the coin, but the fish will bite you for 1 *STAMINA* point of damage. If you are Unlucky, you still get bitten, but you may try again by *Testing your Luck* (you lose 1 *STAMINA* point on each try as you are bitten again). When you eventually get the Gold Piece, or give up, you may continue by turning to **28**.

86

Do you have enough money to afford a room? If so, pay the innkeeper 4 Gold Pieces and turn to **282**. If not, you will have to spend the night on the streets. Turn to **68**.

87

The creature advances to attack, and you can do little about it. Suddenly it looks over towards the shaft of light flooding in from the stairwell. Your eyes are accustomed to the blackness and, when you look over to the light, you cannot be sure what you are seeing. A radiant white female figure seems to stand, glowing in the light. She points back to the coffin. The Deathwraith is terrified of this figure and it returns to the coffin as if directed by some ghostly master. Its movements are becoming very sluggish: it appears that its life-force is being drained. With a last effort, it climbs inside the coffin. You glance back at the figure by the stairs. It has disappeared! Turn to **209**.

88

Where will you kiss next: the forehead (turn to **314**); the right eye (turn to **2**); the left eye (turn to **163**); the right cheek (turn to **334**); the nose (turn to **296**); or the lips (turn to **231**)?

89

Further along the road you come to a fork where you may continue either to the right or the left. The left fork heads out of the city, while the right one leads down a short street towards a large building upon which a signpost reads: THE GAMBLING HALLS OF VLADA. A great Bronze Statue stands in the fork and at its feet is a pot which contains many Gold Pieces. From what you can make out, this must be one of the gods of Kharé and this pot contains offerings from worshippers. Do you wish to continue out of the city along the left fork (turn to **104**), take the right fork and visit the Gambling Halls of Vlada (turn to **56**), or grab a handful of coins from the pot at the feet of the Statue (turn to **221**)?

90

You call out to anyone who may be inside. A voice replies: 'Enter, my friend, but take care as you open the door!' You give the door a shove and step back quickly as a vial of liquid falls on to the floor from the top of the door. You walk forward into the hut. Turn to **43**.

91

You toss the coin into the air and they squabble over it. You may ask them:

Where they have come from	Turn to **180**
How you may reach the centre of the city	Turn to **289**
Whether they have heard of anyone called Vik	Turn to **246**

92

A small pouch drops out of the cabinet and lands on the floor. You open it up and inside you find two small throwing darts. You can attach the pouch to your waist to keep them handy in a battle. Each is enchanted with an explosion spell. You may use them in a fight to throw at your opponent before coming to grips. Each time you use one, throw two dice. If the total rolled is *less than* your *SKILL*, your throw is accurate and you hit your opponent. The dart will explode inflicting 2 *STAMINA* points' worth of damage. If the dice roll is *equal to* or *exceeds* your *SKILL*, you have missed and the dart explodes harmlessly on the floor. Remember that you have only two of these darts. You take the pouch and leave the tent. Turn to **160**.

93

Which of these spots will you try:

Its belt?	Turn to **155**
Its left knee?	Turn to **182**
Its right ankle?	Turn to **212**

94

You curl up in a corner and fall asleep. In the middle of the night, footsteps near by wake you up. Before you know what is going on, you feel a blow to your head and you slump to the ground, unconscious. Turn to **312**.

95

The man steps back and snaps a command at his pet. The BRISTLE BEAST bares sharp pointed teeth and springs at you. Resolve the fight:

BRISTLE BEAST   *SKILL 5*   *STAMINA 7*

If you defeat the creature, turn to **14**. You may cast a spell if you wish:

YAZ	KIL	GUM	GAK	DIM
459	**437**	**378**	**500**	**443**

If you do not wish to fight this creature and anger the man, you may ask him to call off the Bristle Beast and offer him your sword – turn to **229**.

96

You walk over and greet the firemaster. He smiles and hopes you are interested in his fires. He shows you the beauty of white, green, blue and black fire. He is able to create little fires of all these different colours by placing his special rocks, of corresponding colours, into the flames. You are most impressed, as his creations are certainly beautiful, but they would be of little use to you. 'Perhaps you would be interested in one of my special fires,' he says. 'Have a look inside.' If you wish to enter his hut, turn to **108**. If you would rather look at the artist's paintings, turn to **18**.

97

Will you use your magic (turn to **310**) or will you fight the winged beasts (turn to **118**)?

The fight is between a Sprite and a Pixie

98

Through the small crowd, you can see two tiny creatures grappling with each other on the ground. The fight is between a Sprite and a Pixie. Half of the onlookers are cheering on the Pixie while the others are siding with the Sprite. No one is attempting to break the fight up. Will you try to break the fight up (turn to **302**), aid one of the two creatures (turn to **321**), or ignore the incident and continue on your way (turn to **153**)?

99

Are you using a sword (turn to **151**), an axe (turn to **125**), or a bow and arrows (turn to **147**)?

100

The meal – bristle-beast kidneys with a spinach-like vegetable – does not leave a particularly pleasant taste but you force a smile. The creature nods and offers you a mug of dirty liquid to wash it down. You intentionally spill the drink and your host bustles off to get a rag to mop it up. You now have your chance to steal the box. Turn to **29**.

101

You listen at the idol's mouth as it replies to your question. 'The God of Pride is my own brother. He is called Fourga, although he has fallen from favour with our circle of deities and has not been worshipped by the people of Kharé for close on a century.' Is this information useful to you? You may now leave the temple. Turn to **109**.

102

You wait up all night, but no guards come. Lying down on his bench, the old man eventually drifts off to sleep. You must lose 2 *STAMINA* points for missing your rest – and also another 3 *STAMINA* points if you did not eat yesterday.

The guards return shortly after sunrise. Apparently they are satisfied that you are no threat to the city and they release you and the old man. You both head on towards the city but he is a surprisingly brisk walker and has soon left you behind. You watch him turn right at a junction ahead. Turn to **81**.

103

You must either attack them with your weapon (turn to **192**) or you may cast a spell:

GAK	HOW	KIN	DUD	MUD
463	**446**	**349**	**363**	**422**

104

You carry on down the road until a strange sight makes you stop. A mound of earth and rocks, some eighteen inches tall, stands in the centre of the road. It forms a circle, about three feet across, and the surface is black and shiny. Do you want to investigate (turn to **65**) or will you ignore it and continue (turn to **319**)?

105

You go through the murderer's pockets and find 8 Gold Pieces. There is little else of value in the room, but you do find a jar marked 'Poison' which you may take. Another jar contains 'Essence of Bark' which also may be useful. Eventually you leave the building. Turn to **46**.

WIN 20 GOLD PIECES

106

The horse bucks and kicks as it races erratically down the road. You do not manage to halt it, but you do manage to hang on without falling off. Turn to **268**.

107

You may use this artefact to help you locate the lines of the spell. If you follow its direction, it will take you immediately to the vicinity of the last person in this adventure who knows a spell line. When you wish to use it, turn to **319**. Return now to **264**.

108

You enter the hut. In the centre of the room, underneath an open chimney, a fierce fire is burning. Although the blaze is considerable, very little heat actually comes from it, and looking into it you can see a wooden chest resting on the embers in the centre of the flames – but it is not burning! If you are apprehensive, you may leave the hut and continue on your way (turn to **137**). Otherwise you may plot a way to see what treasures might lie in the chest. You could try stepping into the flames, as they are not hot (turn to **130**) or you can cast a spell:

ZIP	TEL	NIP	GOP	MAG
467	**420**	**346**	**478**	**453**

109

You leave the temple and head on. The large North Gate looms up in front of you. This gate is heavily guarded and you will have to make plans for dealing with the guards. Turn to **175**.

110

You enter 'The Wayfarer's Rest'. It is a noisy, bustling place and no one takes much notice as you enter. The innkeeper is behind the bar, trying to serve the numerous creatures all demanding their ale at the same time. The inn is evidently a local for the sailors of the port, as salty types and buxom wenches are laughing together and singing shanties around the tables. You manage to catch the innkeeper's attention. He is a surly, bald-headed man, used to dealing with the rabble from the docks and is surprised at your dress and obviously well-educated tone. 'And what be yer purpose in these 'ere parts?' he asks. You explain you would like a bed for the night, perhaps with some food, and ask the price. 'A room up top'll be 4 Pieces of Gold,' he says. 'And we'll feed yer t'the gills fer another 4.' If you wish to eat before you rest, turn to **331**. If you just want to bed down and perhaps eat your own Provisions, turn to **282**. If you cannot afford to eat or stay, turn to **68**.

111

'Aha! My friend – and enemy!' laughs Flanker as he recognizes you. 'Like myself you also enjoy the fun of the fair! Come, tell me your adventures since we met; or should I say since we *clashed.*' You tell him of your encounters since arriving in Kharé and of your search for the spell lines necessary to open the North Gate. 'Hmmm. I wonder if I can help you,' he says. 'My friend Lortag the Elder lives not far from here. He is a sage and may know something of this spell you require.' If you already have one of the lines to the spell, you have already visited Lortag, so return to **244** and choose what to do at the fair. If you do not have any lines of the spell, you may let Flanker take you to his friend. He will take you back towards the South Gate and along a road where a well-kept house is standing. He will then leave you and you may walk up to the front door – turn to **140**.

112

You open the door cautiously. Inside you can see a small room and on the floor in the centre of this room is a shimmering black circle, some three feet across. Before you have a chance to react, you are grabbed by a strong guard standing just inside the door. 'Another trouble-maker, eh?' says the guard, and he shoves you into the centre of the room. Expecting some sort of splash as you land in the black circle, you are surprised to find that it is not liquid at all. Turn to **270**.

113

Their eyes light up as you pull 15 Gold Pieces from your pouch. 'Must be a noble of some import, eh, brothers?' chuckles the tall guard, taking your money. 'Do what you will then, traveller. We have better things to do, don't we?' He takes the other two off along the wall, leaving you to approach the gate. Turn to **271**.

114

The Flayer snares you with its tentacles. You howl with pain – its tentacles are tipped with nasty stings which will inflict 3 *STAMINA* points of damage instead of the usual 2. Return to **243** and finish the battle, but each time the Flayer succeeds in its attack, its stinging tentacles will inflict this extra damage.

115

'Hmmm, let me see,' he says. 'No, I don't think that is right. I have already tried that rune and it makes no sense. Never mind. Thank you, anyway, for trying. You had better be on your way now. I have enjoyed our chat and wish you luck on your journey. Perhaps this will help you on your way. I believe you will need it if you are to gain any help from the creatures of Kharé.' He hands you a pouch containing what appears to be a handful of green fur. Pulling it out you find that it is a wig. You thank him and he shows you to the door, handing you your weapon on the way out. Turn to **133**.

116

'Were you born yesterday, fool?' replies one of the creatures. Turning its head to look at you, it suddenly cries out: 'A stranger! Brothers, we have a stranger here! Shall we have some fun?' The others turn towards you, apparently 'looking' at you with their closed eyes. They grab you and push you towards the pool. *Test your Luck*. If you are Lucky, turn to **290**. If you are Unlucky, turn to **330**.

117

You take the Golden Locket from the creature. The locket itself is worth around 8 Gold Pieces (you may use it to pay for anything worth up to 8 Gold Pieces in value, but you will not receive change). Inside the locket is a small glowing Sun Jewel which burns brightly with a light of its own. Stow this away in your backpack, add 1 *LUCK* point for surviving the encounter, and continue your journey by turning to **137**.

118

You draw your weapon and chop at the HARPIES as they fly down to attack. The beggar will be helping you with his stick, but he will be of little use since he is blind. Resolve this fight:

	SKILL	STAMINA
First HARPIE	7	6
Second HARPIE	6	6
BLIND BEGGAR	2	8

You may choose who fights whom during the battle, so long as everyone fights someone each round. If you kill the Harpies, turn to **74**.

The Chainmaker grabs a length of chain from the wall. He swings it round over his head and advances towards you. Will you cast a spell?

RAZ	FIX	SAP	RAN	MUD
370	**345**	**502**	**440**	**449**

Or will you fight him?

SVINN CHAINMAKER   SKILL 8   STAMINA 7

If your *STAMINA* becomes reduced to 5 or less, the greater range of his chain will give him an advantage: if you roll equal Attack Strengths for the Chainmaker and yourself, this will count as if he has inflicted a hit on you. If you win, turn to **195**.

You step up to the idol

120

Passing through the streets, you reach another junction where you may either continue straight on (turn to **60**) or turn left (turn to **139**).

121

They watch you carefully as you pass. They are aware that you are ready for a fight but they show no signs of apprehension. Suddenly one of them shouts to the others and they all charge at you. You will have to fight them! Turn to **103**.

122

You step up to the idol. It stands about man-sized before you and an engraved plaque above its head catches your attention. You read it. It seems to be a message which will allow you to talk to the god. Do you wish to try? If so, turn to **252**. Otherwise you may leave the temple by turning to **109**.

123

You get down on your knees. You hear chuckling behind you, and a boot on your rump sends you sprawling forwards into the pool! The splash you are expecting does not happen. Turn to **270**.

124

You recite your spell and wait. A tingle runs down your back as a creaking noise comes from the gate. But rather than seeing the gate open in front of you, you see a ghost-like puff of smoke comes from a wooden box high up on the frame. It skips about in the air like a puppet and you are transfixed watching it. Suddenly it shoots down towards you and, before you can react, it has engulfed you! You cough and sweat, panicking as you realize that this is a SULPHUR GHOST, whose poisonous fumes are suffocating you! As you were warned, the North Gate of Kharé has its own defences, and the uninitiated attempt to open it only at the risk of their own lives. Yours has now been lost . . .

125

The creature approaches as you seize your weapon. Turn to **151**.

126

You call out to the other guards, telling them of the 2 Gold Pieces their companion has taken from you. They look suspiciously at the gate guardian, but he denies your claim angrily and slams his elbow into your stomach. Lose 2 *STAMINA* points and turn to **291**.

127

A little further up the road, you come to a well. A rope hangs down from a pulley deep into the well. You walk up to it and, as you approach, you can hear a woman's voice singing. It seems to be coming from the well itself and to be directed at you:

> 'My dear, your fortune can be told
> If you will cross my palm with gold.'

Do you wish to toss a Gold Piece into the well? If so, turn to **217**. If you'd rather not bother, continue by turning to **319**.

128

The animal looks at you strangely. You try a few soothing words and it calms down, but gives no indication of a response. Eventually you give up with this one-way conversation. As it is now quite peaceful, you may try climbing on to its back (turn to **49**) or you may leave it and continue your journey (turn to **237**).

129

You fall to the floor and pass out, mouthing the words of your prayer. Some time later you open your eyes. The murderer lies dead on the ground. You have no idea of what has happened, but you are certain of one thing: this has been the work of your goddess. But you may not call on her again now until you leave the cityport. You are on your own. Turn to **105**.

130

You step cautiously into the fire. Although the flames do not burn you, the fire begins to sizzle and spit as you enter. As if this were a warning, the firemaster appears at the doorway. He is extremely angry that you should be attempting to steal from his chest and tosses a sooty powder into the fire. You shriek loudly as the fire heats up and you are standing in the middle of a blazing inferno! You leap from the fire with flames sprouting from your clothes. Lose 5 *STAMINA* points for your burns. You pat out the flames from your burning garments and the firemaster orders you out and on your way. Turn to **137**.

131

The street eventually meets another. Turning right will take you into the centre of Kharé and you choose this route. Turn to **165**.

132

You follow a narrow, winding street, which takes you past shops and stalls. It is still early and they will not be open for an hour or two yet, but there are stirrings from within the houses as the day's activities begin. A face appears at one window and seems to watch you pass, although its eyes are closed and you are not sure that you can actually be seen. Another similar creature stands at a doorway, washing in the street. It is thin and spindly, with a long face – and again its eyes are closed. More of these creatures – young males – are hanging about in a group a little further up. They are talking and kicking stones in the gutter. One of them 'sees' you and speaks to the others. This could be trouble. Do you wish to continue as normal and bid them a pleasant day as you pass (turn to **286**); continue, but be ready to defend yourself if they attack (turn to **121**); or take a side street and avoid them (turn to **24**)?

133

A little further along the road you come to a tradesmen's area where potters, weavers and artists are showing their wares outside their huts. Will you stop and look (turn to **3**) or continue (turn to **137**)?

134

In a cupboard in one corner of the room you find two labelled glass containers. The first is labelled 'Blimberry Juice' and you recognize this as a medicinal healing potion. The other is a small vial containing a glue which the Chainmaker uses to hold some of his more delicate chains together. You may take these and either leave the hut (turn to **9**) or keep searching. If you want to look for more treasures, *Test your Luck* again. If you are Lucky, turn to **235**. If you are Unlucky, turn to **19**.

135

The way onwards leads up a street along which a market is being set up. Will you wait to see what is being offered (turn to **226**) or continue up the street (turn to **83**)? If you are short of cash, you may wish to enter a large building on the left with a sign outside reading THE GAMBLING HALLS OF VLADA (turn to **56**).

136

You have now seen how the champion fights. Do you wish to take up the next challenge to try and win the prize of 15 Gold Pieces? If so, turn to **82**. If not, you must now leave the festival (turn to **263**).

137

You continue along the road until you reach a Y-junction where you carry on northwards. Turn to **191**.

138

You continue along the road into a settlement of small huts. As you pass through these homes, ugly creatures who are going about their daily routines watch you. A little way on you come across a body lying face down in the gutter. At first sight this may be a beggar asleep, or some sort of creature in a drunken stupor. Will you investigate to see if it needs any help (turn to **256**) or ignore it and continue (turn to **239**)?

139

Further along the street, you pass a small chapel. From the noises inside, you would guess that a meeting of some sort is going on. Do you wish to investigate (turn to **187**) or continue on your way (turn to **165**)?

140

You stand in front of a solid oak-wood door, decorated with elaborate carvings. In the middle is a great brass knocker and you rap three times. Moments later, the door opens and an elderly man in a gown stands before you. A strange, spiky creature, like a large lizard, nestles next to his leg. You greet him apprehensively. He returns your greeting and appears to be not unfriendly. He will allow you to enter, but not with your weapon. Will you hand him your weapon (turn to **229**) or force your way in with it (turn to **95**)?

141

As you kiss the lips, the idol's eyes flick open. Its lips do not move, but a soft voice comes from its mouth. 'Stranger, you are not of my faith,' whispers the god. 'Nevertheless, you have completed the ritual and I will answer you one question.' What will you ask the god? Who has knowledge of the spell necessary to open the North Gate (turn to **31**)? What will fate have in store for you in the Baklands (turn to **266**)? What is the name of the god of pride (turn to **101**)? How may you best avoid the guards on the North Gate (turn to **193**)?

142

You recite your spell and wait. A tingle runs down your back as a creaking noise comes from the gate. But rather than seeing the gate open in front of you, you see a ghost-like puff of smoke come from a wooden box high up on the frame. It skips about in the air like a puppet and you are transfixed watching it. Suddenly it shoots down towards you and, before you can react, it has engulfed you! You cough and sweat, panicking as you realize that this is a SULPHUR GHOST, whose poisonous fumes are suffocating you! As you were warned, the North Gate of Kharé has its own defences, and the uninitiated attempt to open it only at the risk of their own lives. Yours has now been lost . . .

You have a cell-mate

143

Your backpack and weapons are taken from you and you are locked in a cell, watched over by a Red-Eye guard. You have a cell-mate, a chirpy little ELVIN, who greets you and welcomes you to your new home. He comes from the Elvin valley in the Shamutanti Hills, and since he has been locked in the cell for months now, he is glad of some company. You ask him why he hasn't been able to escape, as Elvins are magical creatures, but he shakes his head, saying that he cannot get any of his spells to work in the gaol. He suspects that a Scramble Spell operates here to neutralize magic.

During your journey, you may have found a key which fits the lock of your cell. If so, you may wait until the guard falls asleep, then use it to escape. Turn to the reference with the same number as the key. If you do not have the key, your only other possible escape is to call on Libra if you have not yet used her help (turn to **30**). Otherwise you will remain in Kharé's gaol for the rest of your life . . .

144

At the junction ahead you may either continue straight on (turn to **165**) or turn right (turn to **120**). Which road will you take?

145

The creature leans over a table and drops the ladle and spoon. Will you show it your weapon and demand that it gives you the box under the table (turn to **273**) or try to hoodwink it by asking if you can buy food (turn to **283**)?

146

The Bronze Statue watches as you toss your gold into the pot. It is torn between attacking you and looking into the pot at your offering. While it is making up its mind, you may escape down one of the streets. Will you take the road leading out of the city (turn to **104**) or the right fork to the Gambling Halls of Vlada (turn to **56**)?

147

You draw your bow and quickly unleash a bolt right at the hideous skull of your attacker. Roll two dice and compare the total with your *SKILL*. If the number rolled is *equal to* or *less than* your *SKILL*, your aim was true. If the number is *higher than* your *SKILL*, you have missed.

You have chosen the only weapon which will harm the evil DEATHWRAITH you are facing. This undead creature can only be harmed by silver weapons and your arrows have silver tips. A hit with an arrow will inflict 2

STAMINA points of damage to it. Resolve your battle in the normal way, but each time you roll a higher Attack Strength than the creature, roll against your *SKILL* score as instructed above to see whether your aim is true. You have 10 arrows and if you do not kill the Deathwraith before your arrows are all used, it will kill you.

DEATHWRAITH   SKILL 9   STAMINA 8

If you kill the creature, turn to **54**.

If you kill the creature, turn to **54**.

148

You follow the road towards the North Gate. You are now leaving Kharé proper and you can see the Great Wall stretching across your path in the distance. One building remains between you and the gate and this looks to be a place of some magnificence. You continue and find that it is a large temple, standing off the road. It is indeed a sight to behold. Totems of the ancient gods line the short path to the temple doors. The building itself is pyramidal, reaching high into the sky. Friezes of gargoyles and sculptures in polished metals ring the temple at each level. Around the doorway, rock-sculptured images of unimaginable creatures seem to guard the entrance. Do you wish to enter the Shrine of Courga (turn to **73**) or will you ignore it and continue to the North Gate (turn to **109**)?

149

The general store offers various items for sale. The following seem of interest to you and you may buy any you wish:

A selection of gauntlets	5 Gold Pieces each
A bottle labelled 'Potion of Mystery'	2 Gold Pieces
Provisions	3 Gold Pieces per meal
A honeycomb of beeswax	2 Gold Pieces
A small vial filled with dust	3 Gold Pieces

Decide which you wish to buy and turn to **199**. If you don't want any of them, you may continue by turning to **170**.

150

You sit down with them on the edge of the mattress. They grin at you with dirty teeth and pass you a pipe. You take several puffs and sit back. The pipe passes round and soon all four of you are staring vacantly into the air. You begin to feel light-headed. But Smoking Weed has an unpredictable effect. Roll one die to see what happens to you:

1. The effect is pleasant and relaxing – gain 2 *STAMINA* points

2. You are overcome with a great feeling of confidence – gain 1 *SKILL* in your next fight

3. You feel sleepy and take a short doze for twenty minutes

4. You cannot resist an urge to do something irrational – give 1 Gold Piece to each of the Elves

5. A feeling of great paranoia swells up within you – deduct 1 *STAMINA* point immediately and reduce your *SKILL* by 1 in your next fight

6. You become violent and draw your weapon – turn to **58**

If you did not roll a 6, turn next to **242**.

151

You draw your weapon and face the creature. As the light catches its face, you can see the horrible skull of a DEATHWRAITH leering at you. Resolve your battle:

DEATHWRAITH   *SKILL 9*   *STAMINA 8*

When you inflict your first hit on the creature, turn to **189**.

WIN 5 GOLD PIECES

A statue outside catches your eye

152

'Thank you for tossing down your wealth
For one more coin I'll grant you health.'

Do you wish to throw in another coin (turn to **295**) or continue on your way (turn to **319**)?

153

You leave the Dwarf village and continue. A little further on you come across a solitary thatched hut. A statue outside catches your eye. It depicts a man (of sorts) with rather long, spindly limbs. Its arms and hands are held together before it, as if it were meant to be praying. Although this in itself is odd, your attention is more taken with a gold locket which hangs around its neck. This looks too precious an artefact to be left hanging on an unprotected statue – it may be very valuable, possibly even magical. Will you:

Take a closer look at the statue?	Turn to **8**
Enter the hut behind the statue?	Turn to **27**
Ignore this temptation and continue?	Turn to **137**
Cast a spell?	

MAG	FAR	GOB	FOF	SUS
482	**413**	**359**	**429**	**472**

154

Eventually a figure appears at the door and you recognize the face. The old man who you met in the guard room looks down at you. 'Aha, my friend!' he says. 'I see you have been caught in our Chainmaker's trap. You are lucky indeed that it is not he who has found you.' The old man agrees to help you out of the net if you will return the 3 Gold Pieces and the bottles of liquid that you have already stolen. You hand them to him and he frees you. 'You had better leave quickly,' he warns, 'before the Chainmaker returns.' You thank him for his help and leave the hut. Turn to **9**.

155

You struggle with the belt, but cannot find any weakness there. The great Statue watches as you pull at the buckle and then claps its hand down upon you, squashing you against its body. Is your *STAMINA* 10 or more? If so, you survive the blow but must reduce your *STAMINA* to 5 points. If your *STAMINA* is below 10, the blow knocks you unconscious and the Bronze Statue will finish you off as you lie on the ground. If you are still alive you must do something quickly to halt the attack. Throw *all* your gold into the pot on the pedestal and turn to **146**.

156

You raise your hand and accept his challenge. 'And who is your god, stranger?' asks the priest. You tell him. 'Libra, the Goddess of Justice? I know nothing of her,' he says. 'You will find Slangg a much more powerful deity. Let us see whether Libra can help you with the challenge of Slangg. If you answer my question correctly, you may ask anything you wish. But if you cannot, you must renounce Libra and become a follower of Slangg. Do you agree?' You nod, and tell him to ask his question.

'Bigfoot the Elder walked south for three furlongs sowing oats, then east for two furlongs sowing corn, then north another five furlongs sowing wheat, and finally south-west for four furlongs sowing hay. Have you got that? Are you ready for the question?' When you are ready, turn to **301**.

157

How much will you offer?

1 Gold Piece each?	Turn to **80**
3 Gold Pieces each?	Turn to **287**
5 Gold Pieces each?	Turn to **113**

If you do not have at least 1 Gold Piece you can give to each of them, you will have to turn to **26** and cast a spell, otherwise you will get no further.

158

You cautiously leave the hut, first looking out into the street. There is no one about. You may now find your way on to the main street and continue. Turn to **89**.

159

You must lose 2 *STAMINA* points for staying awake all night. At daybreak you continue your journey. Turn to **267**.

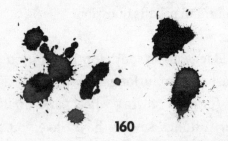

160

You are nearing the centre of Kharé. The huts and dwellings are much more densely located and the roads are dirty. Creatures throng the streets and watch you as you pass. You come to a fork where you may either turn left (turn to **202**) or continue on towards the port area (turn to **165**). Which will you choose?

161

He knows nothing of the North Gate spell and is angry with you for disturbing his work. You must now either leave (turn to **9**), or you may attack him if you wish to search his room (turn to **119**).

162

The bow and arrows, tinderbox and snake-bite antidote are simply as they seem and have no magical properties. The broadsword is difficult to use, but will cause more damage if you strike an opponent with it. If you have bought the broadsword, you may use it in battle. While using it you must deduct 1 from your Attack Strength dice roll, but if you inflict a wound with it, you can deduct 3 STAMINA points' worth of damage instead of the usual 2. You may now leave the market. Turn to **83**.

163

Where will you kiss next: the forehead (turn to **314**); the right eye (turn to **2**); the right cheek (turn to **334**); the left cheek (turn to **88**); the nose (turn to **296**); or the lips (turn to **231**)?

*From a dark alcove, a ghostly white
figure is advancing towards you*

164

You creep cautiously down the stairs. The walls are damp and there is a foul smell of decay in the air. The only sound you can hear is a drip coming from below. At the foot of the stairs, you can see that you are in a large, dark chamber, lit only by the shaft of light coming down the stairway. A coffin stands in the centre of the room and you walk closer to investigate. A creaking sound makes your heart stop! The coffin lid is moving! Spellbound, you watch it inch open, then a movement to your left catches your eye. From a dark alcove, a ghostly white figure is advancing towards you! The shock has startled you so much that you cannot collect yourself enough to cast a spell. Will you draw your weapon (turn to **99**), or run back up the stairs and out of the crypt (turn to **16**)?

165

Night is approaching and you have no wish to spend it in the streets of Kharé. You stop a passing woman and ask the way to a nearby inn. 'Head onwards to the port,' she tells you. 'There is an inn that way. But hurry, stranger, for night is approaching.' You thank her for her help and continue. Eventually you reach 'The Wayfarer's Rest' and step inside. Turn to **110**.

166

This backpack is bigger than the one you currently own and you may replace yours with it. If you do so, the new one will hold more items, and if you are ever instructed 'If you wish to take this item with you, you must leave one behind', you may ignore this and take the new item without losing any of your old ones. Return to **264**.

167

You have received a Lucky Talisman. As long as you have this item, you may deduct 1 point from your dice roll whenever you *Test your Luck*. If you already have a Lucky Talisman, the effect will not be doubled because you have two. You may now leave the tent and continue. Turn to **160**.

168

You check every alcove for possible hiding-places and secret passages, but can find none. Do you wish to check the ornaments for anything worth stealing (turn to **205**) or approach the altar (turn to **122**)?

169

You try the door to the building. It is locked, but the key is in the lock. You turn the key and open the door, stepping inside. But as you do so, the door slams shut behind you and the key turns. You are a prisoner! Turn to **254**.

170

Will you now leave the area, following the road ahead (turn to **153**) or go and join the crowd watching the street fight (turn to **185**)?

171

You try the door. It is open, but you may wish to announce your entry. Will you ask for permission to enter (turn to **90**) or shove the door open quickly to surprise anyone who might be inside (turn to **75**)?

172

You creep round to the back of the house. As you approach the door it suddenly opens in front of you and an elderly man in a dark gown stands before you. His pet, a spiky-skinned lizard-like creature, is at his feet. He is angry and demands to know why you are trespassing in his garden. Nervously, you try to explain that you already tried the front door and thought no one was in. Is your story convincing? Roll two dice and compare the total with your *SKILL* score. If you roll a number *equal to* or *less than* your *SKILL*, turn to **53**. If the number is *higher than* your *SKILL*, turn to **194**.

173

The man becomes angry. 'Ungrateful traveller!' he shouts. 'You may not refuse my hospitality. Join me in a mug of ale. Do this or you shall never leave this house!' Will you reconsider and accept his offer of ale (turn to **34**) or will you fight, if necessary, to escape (turn to **223**)?

174

You find yourself in a dead-end passage. You must turn round and retrace your steps. Which way will you go?

First left, first right, first right, first left,
first right?   Turn to **298**
First right?   Turn to **42**
Third left, first right?   Turn to **77**

175

In front of the gate, the city guards are patrolling in threes. You stop at a tree and pick your moment to approach. When only one group of three stands between you and the North Gate, you step out towards them. They look at you scornfully. 'The gate is closed, simpleton,' says the tallest of the three. 'So turn around and head back into town.' You dare not fight them, as their comrades will soon be back. Will you offer them a bribe (turn to **157**) or cast a spell (turn to **26**)?

WIN 5 GOLD PIECES

Near the centre of the room is an easel

176

You enter the hut, which is decorated with more of the artist's works. Near the centre of the room is an easel and, working furiously at a painting (which is facing away from you), is a brush, seemingly guided by an invisible hand. You cross the room to look at the canvas. The picture it is painting is an image of *you*! Do you wish to wait for the painting to be finished, perhaps to buy it from the artist (turn to **67**), will you stop the brush from finishing its work (turn to **44**), or will you now leave the hut (turn to **137**)?

177

You freeze as your hand feels your empty pouch. The pickpocket has made off with your money – you are now penniless! The crowd is becoming angry and you decide to leave. Will you head over to the dance (turn to **261**), go and see whether the champion has any challengers (turn to **33**), or leave the festival (turn to **263**)?

178

A large, armoured guard with stocky limbs appears at the gate. 'Who wishes to pass?' he growls at you. You tell him you wish to enter to visit your father, giving a false name and claiming to be from Dhumpus. He instructs you to wait while he checks with his officer. You may either wait as he tells you (turn to **225**) or quickly offer him a bribe of 2 Gold Pieces to let you in without question (turn to **59**).

179

Several more inert bodies are thrown down into the hold. But none of the ship's crew appear. After several hours, noises from above indicate that the ship is leaving dock! You still have no escape-route! Slowly, the ship leaves harbour and your fate is sealed. You are destined to become a galley slave, and your quest for the Crown of Kings must be abandoned ...

180

They tell you they have just left their lesson at a scholar's home, a little further up the track. He is their teacher. Turn to **329**.

181

In a small box on the table against one wall you find 3 Gold Pieces. You may take these. You may now either leave the room (turn to **9**) or continue your search. If you continue, you must *Test your Luck* again. If you are Lucky, turn to **134**. If you are Unlucky, turn to **19**.

182

You find a plate on its leg! Quickly, you fit your weapon into the gap around the plate and heave, prising it away from the body. Before the giant creature can react, the plate falls to the ground. As if a valve had been released, a jet of gas blasts from the Statue. The life-giving gas within the giant escapes! It sways and finally topples face down into the street. You have defeated it and are now 18 Gold Pieces the richer! Add 2 *LUCK* points for your good fortune.

Will you head onwards along the left fork out of the city (turn to **104**) or take the right fork to the Gambling Halls (turn to **56**)?

183

The horse snorts nervously as you approach, shifting uneasily. You may try to talk to it (turn to **128**), try to climb on its back (turn to **49**), or leave it alone and continue on your way (turn to **237**).

184

As you make your last turn, your heart sinks as you see you have turned into a blind alley. The footsteps behind you are getting closer. As the creatures turn the corner, you will have a fight on your hands. Turn to **103**.

185

The fight may now have finished during the time you spent at the general store. If so, you continue on your way. Roll one die. If you roll an odd number, turn to **98**. If you roll an even number, turn to **153**.

186

You both sit down and he asks you about yourself and about the world outside Kharé. You answer his questions, but he seems a little distant and you're not sure whether he is really interested or not. You ask him about Kharé. 'Ah, this is a treacherous place,' he starts. 'I can tell you plenty about the dangers of the cityport – but first, would you like some ale?' Will you have a drink with him (turn to **34**) or would you rather be leaving (turn to **173**)?

187

You step into the chapel as a woman and her child are leaving. 'He really is a holy man, mother,' the little one is saying. 'Salen's brother – the lame one – answered his questions yesterday and his leg was healed! He *ran* for the first time in his life!' You are intrigued and you enter the meeting hall. A large number of children and adults are sitting on the floor. At one end, on a platform, is a grey-haired man in white robes talking to the crowd. 'Does anyone else wish to take the test of Slangg?' he asks. 'If you can answer my question, he will grant you any wish. If you cannot, you must renounce your own god and worship Slangg, the God of Malice.' Do you wish to take up this challenge? If so, turn to **156**. If not, you may leave the chapel and continue (turn to **165**).

WIN 20 GOLD PIECES

188

You wander over to one of the dice tables to see what is being played. A dozen gamblers are playing 'Prediction'. You pick up the rules as you watch. The stakes are 1 Gold Piece per throw. You place your stake on any number between one and six. One die is thrown and if your number comes up you win 10 Gold Pieces. It seems that the odds are in your favour. If you wish to play, pay 1 Gold Piece and choose a number (you can hold your finger in one of the boxes below). Throw one die. If this number comes up, you win 10 Gold Pieces. If not, you lose. You may, if you wish, use your luck to help you. *Test your Luck.* If you are Lucky, you may, before you throw the gambling die, nominate any one of the numbers you have not chosen and, if this second number comes up, you may ignore it and roll the die again, thus increasing the chances of your chosen number coming up.

You may not place more than one bet on any roll, and you may only use your *LUCK* once on each bet. You may play five times, and then you must leave the halls, as you must not lose sight of your mission! Turn to **39** when you leave.

189

This powerful undead creature cannot be harmed by normal weapons and it gloats at you as your deadly blow passes through it! Continue the fight:

DEATHWRAITH   *SKILL 9*   *STAMINA 8*

The next time you roll a higher Attack Strength than the Deathwraith, you will not harm it, but you may fend it off enough for you to make an alternative plan. When this happens, you may *Test your Luck*. If you are Lucky, turn to **38**. If you are Unlucky, you must continue the fight and you may *Test your Luck* again next time you roll a higher Attack Strength.

190

A wager-man passes by. You ask what odds he is offering. 'Feeling lucky, eh?' he chuckles. 'I'm giving 3 to 1 on the challenger, or 1 to 3 on the champion. Which do you fancy?' You may place any bet you like on either the Barbarian or the Ogre. For each Gold Piece you put on the Barbarian, you will get 3 back if he wins, but for every 3 Gold Pieces you put on the Ogre, you will get only 1 back if he wins (if you choose the winner, you will also get back your stake money). Place a bet if you wish, then turn to **234**.

191

You reach a junction where several roads converge. You may continue ahead (turn to **297**) or turn to the right (turn to **84**).

192

They laugh as you draw your weapon. One of them opens his eyes and a beam of red fire shoots through the air at your wrist, burning you (lose 2 *STAMINA* points) and causing you to drop your weapon. They advance and surround you and you have no option but to surrender to them. They march you off (with your weapon) to a square building and take you inside. Another creature, similar but a little older, talks to them. It seems that this is their gaol and you are locked inside a cell. Turn to **143**.

193

The god speaks to you through the idol's mouth. 'The North Gate guards are an unruly bunch. Woe betide you if you get involved with them! But they are unscrupulous and care more for their own advantage than the security of the city. You may be able to distract them with a spell. Otherwise offer them 3 Gold Pieces each to look the other way as you approach the gate.' You carefully note this information and leave the temple. Turn to **109**.

194

The man does not believe your story. You can see he is becoming angry. To show you mean no harm, you offer him your weapon to hold while you talk, but he has already decided what he will do. Turn to **95**.

195

You go through the Chainmaker's pockets and find 10 Gold Pieces – apparently chainmaking is a lucrative occupation in Kharé. He also has a neatly folded skullcap in his pocket which may be useful with your spells. On the way out you brush against a dull-coloured chain which catches your attention and you decide to take this with you. Add 1 *LUCK* point and turn to **203**.

196

You had better leave here fast, as Slime Eaters usually feed in groups – the chances are that there are others in this passage. Which way will you go?

First left and then straight?	Turn to **298**
First right, first left, second left, first right?	Turn to **174**
First left, first right, second left?	Turn to **42**

They are thin and spindly, with long faces

197

Outside, a street market is setting up. You may browse through the market stalls (turn to **226**) or just follow the road on out from Kharé (turn to **83**).

198

The early-morning sun is beginning to wake the streets of Kharé. You carry on along the road until you reach a square in the centre of which odd-looking creatures are hanging around a monument of some kind. You walk up for a closer look. The monument is a large arch housing something which must be quite important, judging by the way the onlookers are peering into it. The onlookers themselves are a strange bunch. They are thin and spindly, with long faces. And their eyes seem to be permanently closed! Will you take a closer look at the monument (turn to **204**) or avoid the area and walk round to the other side of the square (turn to **50**)?

199

If you bought the Provisions, you may put these in your pack to eat later. The honeycomb of beeswax is just that. There is a fair amount of wax in the honeycomb. Should you use it in spells you will have enough for the rest of your quest. If you bought any of the gauntlets, turn to **210**. If not, turn to **272**.

200

There is a fair amount of beeswax on this honeycomb; enough to last you for the rest of your quest in any spells you may wish to use it for. Return to **264**.

201

You leave the dance and may now either go over to the ring to see whether anyone is taking on the champion (turn to **33**) or leave the festival (turn to **263**).

202

Following the street, you eventually come to another junction where you may either carry straight on (turn to **131**) or turn down another street to the right (turn to **139**). Which will you choose?

203

The chain is quite a find. It is a magical self-locking chain and you may use it in battle. Whenever you reduce an opponent to 3 or less *STAMINA* points, you can cast this chain around the weakened victim. It will snare your target and lock itself around him, enabling you to step in and finish off the fight without fear of retaliation. Unfortunately, you do not know how to release the chain, so you may only use it once. However, once you have used it, you may *try* to find the hidden catch which will release it by *Testing your Luck* twice. If you are Lucky both times, you release it and may use it again. But the catch cannot be easily found and each time you use the chain, you must *Test your Luck* twice successfully afterwards to release it and be able to use it again. Now you must leave the hut. Turn to **9**.

204

You walk up the steps to the monument and try to get a clear view of what is inside. 'Here, don't push! Be careful!' says one of the creatures. You apologize and peer in. You can see what appears to be a pool of shimmering water inside, although you are not quite sure whether it is really water or not. Will you bend down for a closer look (turn to **123**), ask one of the onlookers what it is (turn to **116**), or back off and leave the square (turn to **275**)?

205

Where will you begin? The temple is garnished with so many valuable artefacts that you are at a loss which to take with you. Sculptures, plates, candlesticks and shields of gold surround you. You step up to a table covered with a silk cloth on which are standing a crystal decanter and four golden goblets. You pick one up and turn it over in your hand. Suddenly you are aware that the humming of the wind has got louder. Looking around, the tapestries are flapping in a strong breeze although previously the air was still. You glance up at the gargoyles – and put the goblet back immediately! All four have turned towards you and are slowly coming to life, flexing their wings behind them. As you replace the goblet, things calm down and the gargoyles resume their positions. Turn to **122**.

206

When the guard eventually falls asleep, you open the cell door. You pick up your backpack and weapons and leave the gaol, running off down the road. The little Elvin escapes with you. He is most grateful to you for freeing him and rewards you by casting a Luck Spell on you. You may restore your *LUCK* to its *Initial* level. You continue along the back streets for a while and eventually you both part company. Turn to **135**.

'Stranger, I cannot thank you enough,' says the beggar. 'Ever since I was cursed with my sightless eyes I have been tormented by those wicked demons.' You talk to him a little longer while you both recover your breath. 'My story is a sad one of fortune to poverty,' he tells you. 'Three years ago I was the Seventh Noble of Kharé until the black-eyed curse befell me ...' You stop him mid-sentence and ask whether he knows anything of the North Gate spell. 'Aye, that I do,' he continues, 'for I was entrusted with one of its lines. If your plan is to leave the cityport that way, perhaps this will help you. My memory is fading but I believe the line was: "By Courga's grace, and ..."' he hesitates. 'And *someone's* pride. Damn! Who's pride was it? One of the gods. "By Courga's grace, and *someone's* pride". I'm sorry, stranger. My memory fails me. I cannot remember which of the gods it was. Perhaps you will find out in Courga's temple, a little further down the road. There you may talk with the God of Grace. But if you do, you risk your life! I can give you one clue: the left eye leads the way. More than that I cannot tell.' You thank him and prepare to leave. Before you go, he says: 'If you are heading out into the Baklands, perhaps this will help. It has been my prized possession for many years, but now I feel I will never use it – I will never leave Kharé – and it will undoubtedly help you on your journey.' He gives you a ring of silver, fashioned as a serpent which coils round your finger. He believes it is a talisman which will protect you from serpents. To find out its real power, turn to reference **130** in the next adventure. This ring is undoubtedly a valuable item. You thank him and collect your belongings, setting off down the road. Turn to **148**.

208

You sneak round the side of the house, checking the windows. Through one window you can see an elaborate study, with the walls lined with books. Evidently the owner is a sage, scholar or wizard. Will you return to the front door (turn to **140**) or try to sneak in through the back door (turn to **172**)?

209

All is peaceful as you rest after your battle. But then a sound makes you look back towards the coffin. A figure is rising from it! But this time the figure is not that of the terrible Deathwraith, but of a very old man. 'Who is it?' he asks. 'Who has put an end to my torment?' Looking round the crypt, his eyes fall on you. 'Stranger, I am in debt to you,' he says. 'For too many years I have been cursed with the living death. Now at last can my soul die in peace. How may I repay you?'

You tell him of your intended journey out of Kharé and across the Baklands. He tells you you will never leave Kharé without the North Gate spell. He knows one line to the spell and tells it to you: 'One lock made out of Golem's hide.' When you tell him more of your quest, he wishes you luck. I cannot be of more help,' he says, 'except for one couplet which I can remember from the ancient days. I have a feeling it may be useful to you. It goes:

> *For sleeping of the sleepless ram;*
> *Seek out the one they call The Sham.*

I am not certain what the "sleepless ram" is, but bear this advice in mind.' You thank him for his help and leave the crypt. Gain 2 *LUCK* points and turn to **16**.

210

The merchant was offering chainmail or leather gauntlets. Which did you buy? Chainmail (turn to **228**) or leather (turn to **238**)?

211

The blade drops and slices cleanly through your neck. Your adventure has ended here . . .

212

No weak spots appear here. But while you are searching, the creature lifts its foot and brings it down towards you. *Test your Luck.* If you are Unlucky, turn to **4**. If you are Lucky, turn to **64**.

It appears to be speaking to you!

213

You leave the hut. The guards have disappeared down the road and you may continue. A little way up you pass a small pond. As you look into it, a small silver fish darts out from behind a stone and looks up at you. Bubbles come from its mouth. It appears to be *speaking* to you! It is hovering over a Gold Piece which presumably someone has tossed into the pond. Will you bend down closer to find out whether it is speaking to you (turn to **320**), snatch the Gold Piece (turn to **85**), continue on your way (turn to **28**), or cast a spell:

HOW	MUD	LAW	MAG	DUD
456	**351**	**375**	**470**	**338**

214

With baited breath, you wait to see whether you have recited the spell correctly. You hear a creaking sound, which gets louder. Suspecting a trap, you look round, but there is nothing to fear: instead a crack of light appears down the centre of the gate! Turn to **511**. You have succeeded in opening the gate and this part of your journey is almost over!

215

If you wish to search the room, you will have to *Test your Luck,* for you will inevitably cause the chains to rattle as you search the room and the Chainmaker may hear you. If you are Lucky, turn to **181**. If you are Unlucky, turn to **19**. If you do not wish to lose *LUCK* here, you may call out for the Chainmaker (turn to **280**) or leave the hut (turn to **9**).

216

'If you wish to find an inn for the night,' he says, 'then if I were you I would not *not* turn right at the junction ahead.' You thank him for his advice and puzzle over his answer as you approach the junction. Remember he is a compulsive liar! Turn to **144**.

217

You throw in your coin and wait for several seconds before you hear it plop into water at the bottom. The well is evidently very deep. The voice sings out again:

> *'If you'll toss one more coin to me*
> *Two wishes will I grant for thee.'*

Do you want to throw in another coin? If so, turn to **152**. If not, you may continue (turn to **319**).

218

You peer round the building and consider your options. A footstep behind you makes you whirl, but too late! Two hands grab your wrists and you look up into the leering face of an armoured guard. His powerful grip holds you tight. Forcing you forward and round the corner, he opens the door of the building and shoves you inside. The lock clicks behind you. Turn to **254**.

219

A rosy-red apple drops from the cabinet to your feet. This appears to be a handsome fruit and you place it in your backpack with your other provisions. However, you are unable to tell that the apple is thoroughly rotten inside. The next time you open your backpack to eat, you will find that it has infected your other Provisions and one meal's worth have been lost (if you have no Provisions at the moment, the rotten apple will merely make a mess inside your pack). You leave the tent and continue your journey. Turn to **160**.

220

Test your Luck. If you are Lucky, turn to **106**. If you are Unlucky, turn to **6**.

221

There are 18 Gold Pieces in the pot. You scoop them out and open your pouch. A creaking noise makes you stop cold! The Statue is coming to life and its arm is sweeping down towards you! You leap out of the way, narrowly avoiding being hit by its palm, and roll on the ground. You stand up and find that the bronze giant has leapt from its pedestal and is advancing towards you. Will you cast a spell (turn to **22**) or face it with your weapon (turn to **299**)?

222

A familiar voice hails you from the other end of the room. 'Ahoy there, my fellow traveller!' says the voice. You turn and grin as you recognize the face of Flanker the Assassin. 'Friend, I cannot stay with you here,' he says – he was just leaving with two other dubious-looking characters. 'But how have things been with you since we last met? You'll find rest here – but are you short of cash? I've just had a run of luck at the Vlada Gambling Halls! Tonight I'm flush! Here, have enough for a drink and a room' – he gives you 5 Gold Pieces – 'Watch the ale here, though. One mug is refreshing, two will make you merry, but three will put you out for the night! Anyway, be seeing you again!' He rejoins his companions and they all leave with linked arms, skipping and singing. You assume he has had two mugs of ale! Return now to **110** and decide what to do next.

223

You step forward to leave. He grabs a bow from the wall, loads an arrow, and aims straight at you. 'You will not escape from Vangorn the Murderer!' he gloats, and draws the string back. You may draw your weapon and attack (turn to **13**) or cast a spell:

LAW	DOP	WAL	SUD	GUM
493	**366**	**383**	**509**	**455**

224

You hunt for signs of any traps. As you walk up to the steps of the altar you stop at a large fancy circle woven into the carpet design. To confirm a suspicion you toss a small stone on to the circle, and smile to see it disappear. You have uncovered a portal which no doubt would have swallowed you had you stepped on to it. You will remember to avoid that spot. Will you now look for any items worth stealing (turn to **205**), search for any signs of life (turn to **168**), or step up to the altar (turn to **122**)?

225

He reappears moments later and, opening a doorway in the gate, lets you in. Motioning quickly to you, he tells you to follow him through the archway inside and along the wall. Suddenly you feel strong hands on your waist and your arms. You struggle, but you are held fast by three guards who bustle you off towards a large building just inside the gate. If you bribed the guard, turn to **36**. Otherwise turn to **291**.

226

Food, weapons and trinkets are for sale in the market. You may buy Provisions for your trip, at a cost of 3 Gold Pieces per meal's worth. Two weapons take your fancy: a bow with a quiver of silver-tipped arrows being offered at 5 Gold Pieces and a fine double-edged broadsword costing 4 Gold Pieces. Thinking of your journey across the Baklands, you are interested in a tinderbox for lighting fires (2 Gold Pieces) and a bottle of snake-bite antidote (3 Gold Pieces). Buy any of these you wish, or can afford, and turn to **162**.

227

You have the strangest dream that you have been captured by a torturer with a sadistic imagination, who is plotting all sorts of horrific fates for you. You wake up with a fright, in a cold sweat.

It is just about sunrise and the early morning light coming through the window lights up your room. Above your head is a sight which makes you freeze! Your movement is restricted by tough leather ties which strap you into your bed and above your neck is the sharp, heavy blade of a guillotine! A chuckle from the bedside catches your attention, and you look over into the squinting eyes of the innkeeper. He laughs loudly. He is after meat for the day's stew, which you may be providing. Perhaps he does not like to kill others himself, or perhaps he just delights in a prolonged suffering, but whatever the reason, he has given you a chance of escape, with a rope fixed round your left wrist. He undoes the tie and you can feel a weight in your hand. You may pull or release the rope. One choice will mean your certain death; the other will raise the blade and allow you to sit up and unfasten your ties. The laughing innkeeper is obviously quite mad, and will give you no help. Will you pull the rope (turn to **211**) or release it (turn to **15**)?

228

With the chainmail gauntlet on you feel strangely confident, and your weapon feels lighter in your hand. You are convinced that your fighting ability will improve with this glove. However, this feeling is a magical illusion caused by the gauntlet and in fact your fighting skill will decrease (deduct 1 point from your Attack Strength rolls in your next fight). After this next fight you will realize the gauntlet's curse and throw it away. Remember this. Did you also buy the vial of dust? If so, turn to **247**; if not, turn to **259**.

229

He takes your weapon and leaves it by the door. He seems genuinely friendly, introducing himself as Lortag the Elder, a scholar and sage. You follow him into his study. Turn to **336**.

230

You scramble back into the crowd away from the dance, with jeers and yells taunting you from the onlookers. A knee butts you viciously in the thigh, causing you to wince and effecting 2 *STAMINA* points of damage. Eventually you fight your way out of the crowd. Turn to **201**.

231

You kiss the idol's lips. As you do so you hear a small click. Your eyes open wide at a sharp stabbing in the back of your throat. You try to call out but the fast-acting poison on the tip of the dart, which has been shot from the golden mouth into your own, silences you. You slump unconscious to the ground in a darkness from which you will not awake. Your journey has ended in this shrine. Such is the price of failing in the kissing ritual of Courga.

232

You find yourself at the end of a blind alley. Their footsteps are coming closer. A fight will be inevitable. You prepare yourself as they turn the corner. Turn to **103**.

233

As you press on up the road, you notice that the huts are becoming smaller. The roadway bustles with Dwarves and other small fellows. It seems from the contemptuous looks you receive as you pass that they are not kindly disposed towards man-sized outsiders. You may stop at the general store in the centre of this area (turn to **149**) or you may continue onwards (turn to **153**). A little further up the street you notice a small crowd gathering round a scuffle between two creatures. If you wish to see what is going on, turn to **98**.

234

The fight starts. You must resolve this battle between the Barbarian and the Ogre:

	SKILL	STAMINA
BARBARIAN	7	8
OGRE	9	12

If you have placed a bet and the battle is going against your chosen winner, you may cast a spell to help him:

KID	JIG	SUN	DUM	YAG
469	**369**	**416**	**507**	**460**

After the battle, turn to **136**, remembering to claim any winnings if you bet on the fight.

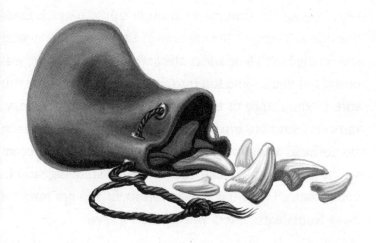

235

Once more you are Lucky and the Chainmaker does not hear you. But he does not leave his hut undefended. As you cross the room, a chain-linked net drops from the ceiling and entangles you. You struggle but this only makes you further entwined in the net. Will you wait to see what happens (turn to **154**) or use a spell to try to free yourself?

PEP	HOW	YOB	WAL	RIS
494	**481**	**388**	**353**	**415**

WIN 5 GOLD PIECES

236

You down the drink and lick the froth from your lips. 'As I was saying,' he continues, 'another thing to watch for is the Portal Traps on the far side of the Jabaji. The nobles live on the North Side and protect themselves with magical portals. If you should fall into one, who knows where you will wind up!' The tone of his voice changes and his eyes narrow: 'But you, my proud friend, will never reach the North Side. Vangorn the Murderer has claimed another victim!' He laughs loudly and you feel a stabbing pain in your stomach. You have been poisoned! You are minutes away from death unless you can cast a spell:

MAG	DOC	FOF	PEP	VIK
430	**376**	**484**	**406**	**340**

Or you can summon the aid of Libra, if you have not already done so in this adventure (turn to **129**).

237

Will you take the left fork (turn to **300**) or continue ahead (turn to **233**)?

238

You have bought yourself a Gauntlet of Weaponry which is blessed with the magical power to help its owner in times of need. While you are wearing this gauntlet during a fight it will aid you, but only if your *STAMINA* has dropped below 5 points. If you are in a battle and your *STAMINA* is below 5, you may choose to re-roll *one* of your Attack Strength dice again (i.e. if you roll a five and a one, you may re-roll the one). Make a note of this.

Did you also buy the vial of dust? If so, turn to **247**. If not, turn to **259**.

239

Beyond this small outskirt settlement you come across a small field surrounded by a rough wooden fence. Half a dozen pigs are grubbing around in this field, well away from a group of creatures huddled round a fire. Will you climb the fence and approach them to see what is going on (turn to **307**) or ignore them and continue (turn to **62**)?

"*There are no losers at Honest Hanna's Cabinet of Fortune!*"

240

You enter the tent and a grubby, bearded man greets you. 'Welcome, welcome, my friend!' he says, somewhat over-enthusiastically. 'And let's see what prize you can win today. There are no losers at Honest Hanna's Cabinet of Fortune!' He takes you over to a large glass cabinet. Inside are all manner of items: jewellery, books, gold, pouches and food. A small Mite is sealed within the cabinet. 'Just 2 Gold Pieces, my friend, and we will see what my little pet will fetch for you!' If you wish to try your luck, give him 2 Gold Pieces and turn to **318**. If you suspect trickery and do not wish to try, you may leave and continue (turn to **160**).

241

You recite your spell and wait. A tingle runs down your back as a creaking noise comes from the gate. But rather then seeing the gate open in front of you, you see a ghost-like puff of smoke come from a wooden box high up on the frame. It skips about in the air like a puppet and you are transfixed watching it. Suddenly it shoots down towards you and, before you can react, it has engulfed you! You cough and sweat, panicking as you realize that this is a SULPHUR GHOST, whose poisonous fumes are suffocating you! As you were warned, the North Gate of Kharé has its own defences, and the uninitiated attempt to open it only at the risk of their own lives. Yours has now been lost . . .

242

You try desperately to start up a conversation, but the smokers are very vague and offer you little information of value. You ask them whether they know of a scholar of some kind in the area. They look dumbly at one another and one of them nods and motions with his hand down the road ahead of you. There is little point in continuing this conversation and you leave. Turn to **213**.

243

As you draw your weapon, the creature bellows loudly and rushes at you. You must fight this FLAYER, who attacks by whipping its head violently from side to side. As it does so, its long tentacles spin at you. If they catch you they will snare you. Resolve your battle:

FLAYER   *SKILL 6*   *STAMINA 7*

When it inflicts its first wound on you, turn to **114**. If you defeat it without injury, you may take the box under the table. Turn to **29**.

244

You press on round a bend in the road. A couple of hundred yards ahead you can see crowds of people – and creatures – sprawling across the roadway. Several tents have been erected which are joined by lines of colourful flags. You are approaching some sort of festival. You decide to continue to see what is going on.

You mingle with the crowd and pass round the various events. A group of musicians is playing a merry jig for a troupe of dancers. Elsewhere a Dwarf has a trained dancing bear on a lead. And from a marked-out ring under a canvas a ruffian is asking for challengers to take on his champion. Do you wish to:

Watch the dancers?	Turn to **261**
Watch the dancing bear?	Turn to **269**
Try your luck against the champion?	Turn to **33**
Leave the festival?	Turn to **263**

245

The poachers are a mixed bunch and ignore the fact that you are a stranger. You tell them a few stories and jokes and they are happy to share their pig with you. You are given a large slice of the pig's leg to eat, which you do. But in trying to eat this, you gulp down a first mouthful which is much too hot for you. You feel a burning in your stomach and you double up, holding your waist. This hot pig has burned your stomach: lose 1 *STAMINA* point now and you will not be able to eat anything else for the rest of the day (if you are given the option to eat, you may not choose it). You thank the group gathered around the fire and stagger off back to the road in pain. Turn to **62**.

246

They look at one another and shake their heads. They have never heard of Vik. One of them shouts, 'Another Gold Piece!' and they all join in, holding out their hands and demanding more money. Turn to **329**.

247

The dust inside the vial is not in fact dust, but grains of sand. You may replace the stopper and take this vial with you. Turn to **259**.

248

'Brothers and sisters!' he shouts. 'We have a new convert to the God of Malice!' As you have agreed, you must now renounce your faith in Libra and worship Slangg. This means that you will never again be able to call on aid from Libra. You are on your own in Kakhabad for the rest of your adventure. After taking your vows, you may leave the chapel. Lose 2 *LUCK* points and turn to **165**.

249

The door swings open and you jump inside. The small crypt is empty! But against the far wall is a narrow stone staircase that leads down to a lower level. Will you follow this downwards (turn to **164**) or have you had enough of this place (turn to **16**)?

250

You take a deep breath and duck down into the foul sludge. When you come up for air, the deluge has gone and you can clamber out of your predicament. This experience has made you ill and you must deduct 3 *STAMINA* points. You clean yourself off as best you can and now you must try to find a way out. Will you:

Continue ahead, take the first right, then
first right again? Turn to **298**

Continue ahead, take the first left, then
left again? Turn to **42**

Continue ahead, take the first left and then
straight on? Turn to **174**

251

Going through their pockets, you find 5 Gold Pieces. A noise outside startles you and you turn towards the door. Will you investigate (turn to **213**) or ignore it and continue to search the room (turn to **305**)?

252

As the message suggests, you must kiss the idol's face. Where will you kiss first: its forehead (turn to **314**); its right eye (turn to **2**); its left eye (turn to **284**); its right cheek (turn to **334**); its left cheek (turn to **88**); its nose (turn to **296**); or its lips (turn to **231**)?

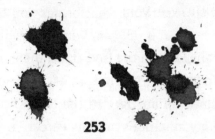

253

He buys you another mug of ale and you drink again with him. Add 2 *STAMINA* points as you are now getting quite light-headed and the two of you are laughing together. He knows the cityport well. You press him for more information on the holders of the spell lines, but apart from telling you that one of the people you seek fell recently out of favour with the Third Noble of Kharé (rumoured to be a Vampire) and is now cursed with living death, he knows little. You are interested in a story of one of his friends who tried to talk to Courga, one of the gods, and was killed in the temple for daring to kiss the god on the cheek. He tells you also of some of his adventures on the high seas. He offers another drink. Will you instead offer to buy him one (turn to **306**) or tell him you must now be getting some sleep (turn to **86**)?

You are in a stone hut with barred windows. A bench against one wall is the only piece of furniture in the room and on this bench sits an old man. Dressed in dirty robes, he stands and greets you, holding out his right hand. You realize that this is his *only* hand as his left sleeve hangs limply by his side. 'And what brings you to this wicked place?' he asks. You tell him you are heading out of the city and he nods. 'Then I take it, stranger, that you are a sorcerer. Indeed, this was my profession before fate – with a little help from an Ogre in the Schanker Mines – put an end to my ambitions and my career.' He indicates his missing limb. 'Only a sorcerer would know the spell to pass through the North Gate.'

You look a little puzzled. 'You know the spell, do you not?' he asks. When you *still* look puzzled, his eyes widen and he shakes his head. 'Then I'd better explain . . .'

He goes on to tell you that the North Gate is wizard-locked to protect the city from Bakland raiders. The magical lock opens only when a particular magical incantation is recited before it. Only the First Noble of Kharé knows the spell in its entirety, although its four lines are known, one each, by four leading citizens. This prevents each one from opening the gate alone, which ensures the security of Kharé. You ask him about these 'leading citizens' but he knows little of them. He has heard, however, that one is a scholar.

You ask him also about this building and he reassures you. Guards will return in a day or so to release you once they have verified you are not an enemy of the cityport. Will you now wait for their return (turn to **260**) or cast a spell to free yourself?

ZAP	POP	FIX	DOP	FIL
371	**504**	**486**	**432**	**344**

255

'That one!' he scoffs. 'Why, even my own pupils could see that that is not the right rune! Goodness me, I do believe you will have to rely on a lot of luck to get you through your journey!' He laughs loudly. You decide it is about time for you to leave. 'Before you go, my friend, I will give you something to give you the luck you will need. Here, take this.' He gives you a small oatmeal cake and tells you that, if you eat half of this cake, your luck is guaranteed at any time. In the journey ahead, if you are called on to *Test your Luck,* you may instead eat the cake. If you do so, you will automatically be Lucky without having to make a dice roll or deduct from your *LUCK*. The cake will work twice, once for each half. You thank him for his kindness and leave his house, collecting your weapon on the way out. Turn to **133**.

WIN 10 GOLD PIECES

256

You walk up to the limp body on the ground. Nobody in the street seems to be taking any notice of it and you bend down closer. You put your hand on its shoulder and shake it. No response. You hold its arms and turn it over. As its face swings round, you jump back aghast!

You are looking at a semi-decayed corpse! Its rotting head is half skull, half rotten flesh and you stifle a shriek of horror. As you turn away from the horrendous face, an evil smile spreads across what is left of its lips and it springs to its feet! It leaps on you, giving you no time to do anything but draw your weapon and attack it:

LIVING CORPSE   *SKILL 6*   *STAMINA 6*

You must fight this creature. When you have inflicted your first hit, turn to **11**.

257

Which spell will you choose?

DIM	BAM	BAG	DUD	WOK
417	**347**	**398**	**445**	**342**

If you know none of these, you must draw your weapon and attack. Turn to **243**.

258

Test your Luck. If you are Lucky, you clear the circle and land in the arch of the doorway (turn to **317**). If you are Unlucky, your jump does not take you quite over the circle (turn to **288**).

259

Did you buy the Potion of Mystery? If so, you may swallow the liquid (turn to **281**). If you did not buy it, turn to **170**.

260

You wait for the rest of the day but the guards do not return. As night falls, you must decide about food and sleep. Will you eat from your Provisions? If so, turn to **308**. If not – or if you cannot – turn to **333**.

261

Joining in with the crowd, you watch the dancers step and spin to the musicians' tune. The pitch builds up and the crowd joins in, clapping in time to the music. With admiration for the skill of the dancers, you too get carried away and begin to clap and stomp your feet. Add 1 *STAMINA* point for your enjoyment. The dancers twirl round the audience and grab one or two onlookers, pulling them into the dance, much to the merriment of the crowd. One of the dancers grabs you and pulls you into the circle. Will you join in with the dance (turn to **17**) or will you pull away from your partner, not wishing to embarrass yourself (turn to **40**)?

262

Roll one die, to see what they manage to steal from you:

1, 2 or 3 They take 3 Gold Pieces (or as many as you have if you have less than 3)

4, 5 They take all your Provisions

6 They take the *largest item* in your backpack

If you rolled a double six when *Testing your Luck,* they manage to free the straps on your backpack and take the whole thing, racing off down the road. You follow after them and find the discarded backpack, but you have lost all your possessions!

If you have now lost something of value, you may try casting a spell to recover it:

TEL	RAN	KID	SIX	GOB
448	**396**	**404**	**506**	**426**

Otherwise turn to **61**.

263

You leave the festival, but as you pass one of the tents, an interesting sign takes your eye: CABINET OF FORTUNE – TRY YOUR LUCK – A PRIZE FOR ALL – ONLY 2 GOLD PIECES. If you wish to see what is going on, turn to **240**. If not, turn to **160**.

264

'Good, good!' squeaks the Gnome. 'Let's see what sort of a bargain we can give you today.' The items he has on offer are listed below. You must select four items from your own Equipment (you may not choose Gold, Provisions or your weapon) and list them, allocating each a different number between 2 and 5. You may select two of his articles on offer. For each of your choices, roll one die. If you roll a

1. He is not interested in anything you are offering. He will instead accept any article still left on your Equipment List (i.e. one which you have not listed for barter).
2–5. He will take the article you have offered, which corresponds to this number as instructed above.
6. He wants two items in exchange for his one. Roll again twice (ignoring 1s and 6s) to see what he wants.

If you wish to go for two of his articles and, on the second roll, you roll the number of something you have just given him, you are lucky and he throws this second item in, without asking you for anything else in exchange.

If you do not have enough Equipment, or you do not wish to use all your own possessions, you may cast a spell:

DOC	MAG	GOB	DUD	ZEN
419	**360**	**386**	**490**	**457**

The following are available. You may choose two:

Bamboo Flute (**304**) Bag of Goblin Teeth (**45**) Lucky Talisman (**20**) Enchanted Compass (**107**) Large Backpack (**166**) Beeswax (**200**)

The references next to each object are for turning to if you acquire it. When you have finished with the little Gnome, turn to **158**.

You find nothing. The bronze giant swats you off with a powerful blow, knocking you through the air. Lose 4 *STAMINA* points. Return to **326** and choose again.

266

You put your ear close to the idol's mouth to hear the god speak its answer. 'Stranger,' it says, 'there is no fate in store for you in the Baklands. You do not have enough information about the spell needed to open the North Gate. You had better retrace your steps and start your journey again.' This answer is indeed a disappointment. You may either begin this adventure again or head onwards to the North Gate in the hope that the god is mistaken (turn to **109**).

267

Did you eat at all yesterday? If not, you are now famished and must deduct 3 *STAMINA* points. If you did eat, you suffer no penalty. Turn to **325**.

268

The horse gallops off down the road the way you came and you hang on desperately. It is heading towards a scattering of huts when a small scaly creature runs across the road in front of it, causing it to rear up. You slide off over the horse's backside and land on the ground. Luckily, you are unhurt. The horse whinnies and races off along a different track as you pick yourself up. Will you approach a hut on the left of the road (turn to **66**) or another on the right (turn to **171**)? If you would prefer, you may ignore these and continue past them (turn to **294**).

A crowd has gathered around the Dwarf and his bear

269

A crowd has gathered around the Dwarf and his bear. In one hand he holds a lead which is fastened to a ring through the bear's nose. By jerking this, he is able to make the bear stumble round in a sort of dance. In the other hand he holds a small pipe to his lips and is playing a lively tune. The bear is by no means a graceful dancer and the crowd is laughing loudly at its clumsy steps. You watch for several minutes. Suddenly a cry comes up from the audience: 'My gold is gone! *Pickpocket!* Beware the pickpocket!' You, and the rest of the crowd, spin round towards the voice. You can see a small creature darting off away from the crowd down the road and into one of the tents. There is little hope of his being caught. You turn back to the Dwarf and his bear just in time to see them vanishing! This show has been nothing but an illusion, created to distract the audience while the pickpocket steals gold. Other creatures in the crowd are checking their gold and several of them have been victims of the pickpocket. Do you still have your Gold? *Test your Luck.* If you are Lucky, turn to **63**. If you are Unlucky, turn to **177**.

270

You float slowly down through the air, turning over and over ... In the pitch blackness you cannot see a thing. Then, as if you were falling down a tunnel, you see a spot of light in the distance, which grows larger as you fall towards it. Eventually you emerge ... to a fate that is almost worse than death.

Evidently you are in the sewers deep underneath Kharé. Tunnels disappear in all directions and the stench is unbearable. You have landed in a disgusting pile of unbelievable filth: slime, excrement, sludge, dung and dregs – and you are up to your neck in it! Before you can even try to crawl out of the quagmire, a splashing sound to your left draws your attention to a small opening in the wall right next to your ear. Coming pouring down this shute is a torrent of liquid sewage and pigswill. Within moments it will burst from the shute straight into your face! You must decide quickly: *will you duck to avoid it?* If you wish to duck, turn to **250**. If you could not bear to duck, turn to **327**.

271

You step up to the dark North Gate of Kharé. A few yards from the gate you stop dead as a phantom voice speaks to you. 'Halt, stranger!' booms the voice. You look around, but no one is near. It is the gate itself which is speaking to you! 'You may not pass through this gate, for it is wizard-locked. If you do not know the unlocking spell, your next step forward will mean your instant death!'

Do you know the four lines of the spell which will open the gate? If you do, arrange them in the correct order and speak them at the gate. Three numbers are hidden within the spell. If you write these down in order, the result will be a three-digit number. Turn to the reference with this number to see whether you have recited the spell correctly. If you do not know the four lines of the spell, you will have to start again, this time being careful to follow all the clues which will lead you to the keepers of the spell lines …

272

Did you buy the vial of dust? If so, turn to **247**. If not, turn to **259**.

273

Roll two dice. If the total is *higher than* your *SKILL* score, turn to **303**. If you roll *lower than* or *equal to* your *SKILL*, turn to **313**.

274

'Let me see that,' he says. 'Why do you think this rune is correct?' You explain that the others represent spots on a gambling die. This rune is the missing one. 'Of course!' he exclaims. He is very excited at your having solved his problem and enthusiastically agrees to help you in your quest. 'I know of only one line in the spell you require,' he starts, 'and it reads as follows: "So tumblers two sealed deep inside." I know not who keeps the other three lines, but they are all leading citizens. In this city, often the creatures know more than the men-folk, so this gift may be of use to you.' He hands you a small pouch with what appears to be a handful of green fur inside. You pull it out and find that it is a wig, which may be useful in your spells. Thanking him, you decide to press on, collecting your weapon on the way out. Restore your *LUCK* to its *Initial* level and turn to **133**.

275

You back away from the monument and make your way cautiously around it to the far side of the square. Turn to **135**.

276

You step back and the broken fragments of the corpse's body flail about you ineffectually. Eventually they settle on the ground and re-unite, leaving the corpse looking as though it has been run over in a chariot race. A head appears at the doorway of a nearby hut and beckons you over. Some Gnomes have been watching the battle from their hut and they thank you for ridding their neighbourhood of the gruesome creature. Their children may now play in the street without danger.

They press upon you 5 Gold Pieces as a reward and ask whether there is anything they may do to help you. You tell them of your quest. They agree you will need to find the four spell lines to leave the cityport, and suggest you may get help from the priest straight ahead, on your way into the centre of town. They can also offer you items that may be useful with your spells and you may accept from them either a medicinal potion, or a bag containing three small round pebbles, or a vial of sand (a rare commodity so far from the sea). You may choose one of these. Then turn to **239**.

277

They taunt you to do something about it. You will have to force them to return the Gold to you. One of them casually blinks at the ground and as his eyelids open you can see his eyes – two burning red balls of flame! Will you prepare to attack them (turn to **103**) or leave them and continue (turn to **89**)?

278

There are no likely weaknesses here. The giant creature kicks backwards and knocks you through the air, so that you land awkwardly on the pedestal. Lose 3 *STAMINA* points. Return to **326** and choose again.

279

A piece of mouldy goat's cheese drops at your feet. The smell is awful. You can throw this away, or take it with you. If you wish to keep it, you must lose 1 *STAMINA* point for as long as it is in your possession. You turn angrily at the man, but he shrugs his shoulders and tells you it was purely a game of luck. You leave the tent and continue your journey. Turn to **160**.

280

As you wait you can hear shuffling beyond the far door. Eventually a figure appears and you recognize the Chainmaker as a SVINN – one of the man-orcs from the village of Torrepani. He addresses you gruffly and asks whether you are interested in buying his chains. Will you select an interesting-looking chain and ask how much he wants for it (turn to **332**) or ask him if he can help you find the spell to open the North Gate (turn to **161**)?

281

You gulp down the potion and wait for something to happen. Your head feels dizzy and you pass out, collapsing on to the floor. When you re-awaken and look around, your surroundings have changed and passers-by are looking at you with surprise. Turn to **294**.

282

You wander upstairs to your room. The room is dark and you have been given no candle, so you grope around for the bed and sit on it. You may, if you wish, eat Provisions here which will restore 2 *STAMINA* points if you have not yet eaten today (1 *STAMINA* point if you have already eaten). You lie back on your mattress and fall asleep. Turn to **227**.

283

Its eyes narrow as it looks at you, sizing you up. A muffled sound comes from its head and words which you can barely make out reach you. It offers you a meal, but this will cost you 5 Gold Pieces. If you wish to continue your deception, you will have to buy a meal – gain 2 *STAMINA* points if this is your first today (or 1 *STAMINA* point if you have already eaten) – and turn to **100**. If you do not wish to pay, or cannot afford it, you will either have to leave (turn to **294**) or attack it. If you attack it with your weapon, turn to **243**; if you wish to cast a spell, turn to **257**.

You look into the air and see two winged beasts hovering over y

284

Where will you kiss next: the forehead (turn to **314**); the right eye (turn to **78**); the right cheek (turn to **334**); the left cheek (turn to **88**); the nose (turn to **296**); or the lips (turn to **231**)?

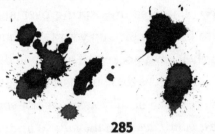

285

You toss him a coin and he thanks you for your kindness. You sit down for a moment to talk to him. Suddenly you are both alarmed by a screeching noise in the sky above you. 'No!' he cries. 'Not those god-cursed Harpies! Will they never cease their torments?' You look into the air and see two winged beasts hovering over you: They are ugly, dark-skinned creatures with sharp talons on the ends of their arms and legs. You both spring to your feet. You are not quite sure what to do, but the beggar grabs his stick and flails it about blindly in the air. 'They are after my gold!' he shouts to you. 'Have they no pity on a blind man? Oh, stranger, can you *see* the evil rascals? Can you help me?' One of the Harpies darts down from the sky and clips him on the head, knocking him over. Will you decide to help the old man (turn to **97**) or do you prefer not to get into this fight and run off down the road (turn to **148**)?

286

They scoff at your pleasantries. One of them trips you up and sends you sprawling in the street. As you fall, your pouch opens and Gold Pieces spill into the road (if you have no Gold, lose 2 *STAMINA* points for a bruised knee and turn to **89**). The creatures spring over and around you, claiming to help you pick up your Gold, but actually putting it into their own pockets. Throw one die. This is the number of Gold Pieces that you manage to grab before they join in and this will be all you salvage of your gold. If you wish to *Test your Luck,* you may do so and, if you are Lucky, you can throw the die again and grab this many Gold Pieces from the creatures before they pocket them (obviously you cannot collect in total more Gold than you had originally). Will you challenge them to return the Gold they have stolen (turn to **277**) or leave them alone and continue (turn to **89**)?

287

They look at each other, trying to decide whether they could get any more Gold out of you. 'All right, traveller,' says the tall one, 'but whatever you want to do, make it quick.' They take your offering and wander off away from the gate. You now have a short time in which to step up to the gate and try to open it. Turn to **271**.

288

Your feet touch nothing on the circle and you fall down through it. It is a Portal Trap and you fall slowly downwards through the blackness. Turn to **270**.

289

They tell you that you are heading the wrong way. You must turn back and take the other road onwards. Do you wish to do this? If so, turn to **233**. If you would prefer to continue the way you are going, turn to **329**.

290

You manage to squirm out of their grip. They turn towards you, looking for a fight. Will you cast a spell:

GAK	VIK	KIN	HOT	TEL
367	**462**	**382**	**434**	**495**

Or will you fight them with your weapon (turn to **309**)?

They frogmarch you across to the building and shove you inside, locking the door behind you. You gather yourself together and look around. Turn to **254**.

292

You follow the road to a group of huts. The old man nipped inside a large, dirty-looking hut on the left. You may follow him if you wish (turn to **66**) or you may instead enter a hut opposite, from which an interesting smell is floating across the road (turn to **171**). Otherwise you may continue, passing the huts (turn to **294**).

293

The Sprite is most grateful and asks how it may help you in return. You tell it of your mission and your wish to learn the spell to open the North Gate. It does not know anything about the spell, but can suggest someone who may be able to help. It leaps into the air and flutters its wings, telling you to follow. The little creature takes you off the road, between the Dwarfs' houses and across an expanse of scrubby wasteland. Eventually you approach another road and the Sprite leaves you, pointing to a large house of stone and mortar. You may add 1 *LUCK* point for the find. Will you approach the house? If so, you may go up to the front door (turn to **140**), creep round the back (turn to **208**) or continue down the road (turn to **133**).

294

Along the road ahead of you, you can hear the mixed sounds of a large crowd. Perhaps you are heading towards a market or fair of some kind. You arrive at a junction where you may either continue (turn to **244**) or turn to the left (turn to **328**). Which way will you choose?

295

*'Pray throw me down another piece
And all your hurting soon will cease.'*

Do you wish to throw down another coin (turn to **315**) or continue on your way (turn to **319**)?

296

Where will you kiss next: forehead (turn to **314**); the right eye (turn to **2**); the left eye (turn to **163**); the right cheek (turn to **334**); the left cheek (turn to **88**); or the lips (turn to **231**)?

297

You are now entering the centre of Kharé proper, and the buildings and homes are much more closely grouped together. Humans and creatures skulk in the streets. It is late afternoon and you had better start thinking about where you will spend the night. You are walking along at about the same pace as a youngster and the two of you start chatting. He is a strange fellow, who calls himself Slangg. He tells you he lives beyond the North Gate of Kharé. He also tells you remarkable stories about his mother being a Skunkbear, about how he eats nothing but rats' brains and that he is a personal servant to the First Noble of Kharé. You soon realize that he is a compulsive liar! *Everything he says is untrue.* Eventually you reach a junction near his destination. Before he leaves you may ask him for advice. Will you ask him how you may most quickly reach the nearest inn (turn to **216**), or whether he can direct you to one of the holders of the lines to the North Gate spell (turn to **51**)?

298

You find yourself in a dead end. Will you:

Turn around and take the first right?	Turn to **77**
Turn around, take the first left, then second left?	Turn to **42**
Turn around, take the first left, then straight on?	Turn to **174**

A group of young Orclings are scurrying down towards you

299

You draw your weapon and race towards the creature. It moves slowly. You are able to get in close and swing a hefty blow up at its waist. Your weapon clangs loudly on the bronze and sends a painful shock through your arms. Lose 1 *STAMINA* point. The BRONZE STATUE swings its hand at you and although you leap out of the way, it catches you in the back and winds you. Lose another 2 *STAMINA* points. You must fight the Statue:

BRONZE STATUE   *SKILL 10*   *STAMINA 15*

When you strike your first blow, turn to **326**.

300

You follow the road, which narrows. A group of young Orclings are scurrying down towards you, shoving and hitting one another. Seeing you, they rush up and surround you, and ten little voices are pestering you: 'Hello. One Gold Piece?' Their hands are poking at you, held flat to receive your donation. Will you toss them a Gold Piece (turn to **91**) or ignore them and press onwards (turn to **329**)?

WIN 20 GOLD PIECES

301

'The question is ...' and here the priest pauses for effect. The tension mounts in his audience. 'The question is ... What was his favourite colour?'

You protest strongly, as his question is most unfair, whereupon the crowd bursts into laughter. You smile sheepishly as you realize you have been caught by what must be one of his standard hoaxes. He is certainly quite a showman for a priest!

'All right then, Analander,' he starts. You are amazed. *How did he know you were from Analand?* He asks his question: 'In Bigfoot's family are 6 sons. Bigfoot is nearing the end of his life and he wishes to divide his wealth exactly among his sons. He gives 5 Gold Pieces to his second youngest son, 13 Gold Pieces to his eldest and 9 to the fourth youngest. Do you know how much the other sons received and how many Gold Pieces he possessed in all?' Think carefully about your answer. When you have decided, call out your answer and turn to the reference corresponding to that number. If you cannot answer his question, turn to **248**.

302

Do you wish to cast a spell to break the fight up?

NIF	WIK	FIX	DOZ	GOD
391	**379**	**447**	**410**	**400**

Or do you want to step in and separate the two combatants (turn to **311**)?

303

Your threat does not worry the creature. It steps towards you. You must attack it. Turn to **243** if you wish to fight with your weapon. Turn to **257** if you will cast a spell.

304

The flute has a pleasant tone and is otherwise quite normal. This may keep you amused in the next stage of your journey. Return to **264**.

305

Underneath the mattress in the corner you find a mask made out of black wood, carved to resemble one of the gods worshipped by the Black Elves. You may take this with you. There is little else in the room and you leave the hut. Turn to **213**.

306

He accepts your offer and you stagger off to the bar. You buy two mugs of ale (1 Gold Piece each – if you haven't enough money, you couldn't offer him a drink, so turn to **86**). You both become very drunk. He sees a friend behind you and stands to wave at him. But rather than greet his friend, he pulls out a cudgel from his belt and brings it down on your head. You slump unconscious on the table. Turn to **312**.

307

You stride across the field towards a group of odd-looking creatures gathered around a fire. Roasting on a spit over the fire is a large pig which they have killed. This may be a suitable place for you to rest and eat Provisions (do this if you wish and deduct 1 Provision point – add 2 *STAMINA* points if this is your first meal today, or 1 *STAMINA* point if you have already eaten). Otherwise you can befriend them and, when the pig is cooked, join in their feast for a free meal (turn to **245**). If you are not interested in eating the pig, you may return to the road and continue (turn to **62**).

308

You may eat a meal and will thus gain 2 *STAMINA* points. However, if you do so, you will have to share your food with the old man as he is hungry and has given you valuable information. Give him one meal's worth of Provisions (if you have only enough Provisions for one meal, you will have to share it with him and will gain only 1 *STAMINA* point), then turn to **333**.

309

As you draw your weapon, one of them opens his eyes. Behind his eyelids burn two balls of flame and, when he looks you in the eyes, a line of fire shoots into your face. You scream and hold your hands to your eyes, but it is too late. Permanent blindness is your penalty for tangling with the RED-EYES and you will not now be able to continue your mission.

310

Which spell will you use?

DIM	PEP	MAG	GOB	WOK
473	**480**	**433**	**365**	**389**

If you know none of these, you will have to use your weapon (turn to **118**).

311

The crowd boos you as you step forward. You grab each of the little creatures and hold them apart. They are not at all grateful and instead both turn to attack you! Resolve this combat:

	SKILL	*STAMINA*
SPRITE	5	6
PIXIE	5	5

They will both attack you at the same time. Roll for your own Attack Strength and roll once for each of the two creatures. If your Attack Strength is higher than either of theirs, you may choose which you will inflict the wound on. If one of their Attack Strengths is higher and the other lower, you will wound the lower, but be hit by the higher. If both their Attack Strengths are higher, they will both wound you. This will not be a fight to the death on their part (although they will try to kill you) – they will give up and drop out of the fight once their own *STAMINA* scores fall to 2. When this fight is over, the crowd disperses and you may continue. Turn to **153**.

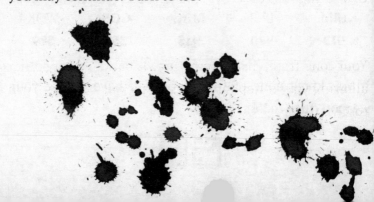

312

You open your eyes and feel a pain thundering in your head. Lose 2 *STAMINA* points. You raise your hand and rub the back of your neck as you take in your surroundings. The ground is rocking softly and either you have not yet recovered from the blow, or you are in a ship of some kind. The wooden pit you are in, with an opening at the top, suggests the latter. Other bodies are sprawled on the floor around you and you shake one awake. He is in the same state as you are, and rubs his head with his hand. You ask him where you are and together you come to the conclusion that you have been waylaid: captured to be crew on a slave galley. There is no hope of reaching the door high in the ceiling. Do you wish to cast a magic spell?

RAP	VIK	ZAP	ZEN	DUD
501	**402**	**464**	**343**	**438**

Or will you wait to see what happens to you (turn to **179**)?

313

Your tone frightens the creature. It backs into a corner allowing you to step forwards and pick up the box. Turn to **29**.

314

Where will you kiss next: the right eye (turn to **2**); the left eye (turn to **163**); the right cheek (turn to **334**); the left cheek (turn to **88**); the nose (turn to **296**); or the lips (turn to **231**)?

315

'Just one more coin, that's all I ask
I'll give you help with any task.'

Will you throw down another coin (turn to **152**) or continue on your way (turn to **319**)?

316

You free yourself from the little urchins and continue up the track. A short distance further on you come across a largish home made of stones and mortar. This place looks quite important. Will you walk up to the front door (turn to **140**), creep around the back of the house (turn to **208**), or continue straight on (turn to **133**)?

317

You may now try to enter the crypt. Will you shove the door aside and rush in, to surprise anything that might be inside (turn to **249**), delve into your pack to pull out something which may be useful (turn to **7**), or cast a spell?

SUS	DOC	FOF	BIG	FAK
390	**499**	**476**	**452**	**424**

WIN 5 GOLD PIECES

318

He takes your money and presses a small button on the side of the cabinet. With a squeal, the Mite leaps from its perch and flutters around over the prizes in the cabinet. Selecting one, it flies over to a shute at the front of the box and drops the prize in. This then drops out of the box at your feet. What have you received? Roll one die. If you roll a

1. Turn to **279**   3. Turn to **167**   5. Turn to **71**
2. Turn to **5**   4. Turn to **92**   6. Turn to **219**

You may wish to *Test your Luck* here to try to ensure you receive a valuable, rather than a worthless, prize. If you *Test your Luck* and you are Lucky, you may *choose* one of the six options from the table above instead of rolling the die. True, you don't know which are valuable and which are worthless, but as a hint, only one of numbers 1-3 is a valuable item, but two of numbers 4–6 are. So your chances are better if you choose a 4, 5 or 6.

319

You are now leaving the centre of the city. The street turns into a dirt track which winds from Kharé past a small settlement of huts and out past a tall building. In the distance, you can see the Great Wall of Kharé and the North Gate. At a tree stump along the way you may stop and eat provisions. If you do so, add 2 *STAMINA* points if this is your first meal of the day (1 *STAMINA* point if you have already eaten). Just outside the group of huts, you come across a blind beggar who asks you for alms. Will you give him a Gold Piece (turn to **285**) or will you press on towards the gate (turn to **148**)?

320

You bend down close and put your ear to the surface of the water. The little silverfish spits at you and a drop of water lands on your cheek. If fishes could laugh, you would swear this fish was chuckling at you! Again it mouths bubbles at you. A sound comes over but the bubbles obscure it. It sounds a little like *'Bwrthhrs'*. But what can this mean? The fish swims back behind its rock and you may now either continue on your way (turn to **28**) or try to pick up the coin (turn to **85**).

The crowd is not happy with your intervention. You must choose your side: the Sprite or the Pixie, and resolve the battle:

	SKILL	STAMINA
SPRITE	5	6
PIXIE	5	5

During each Attack Round, compare your Attack Strength with that of your chosen ally. Whoever has the higher will be the main fighter in that round (conduct this as normal), but if the remaining combatant (e.g. your ally, if yours was the higher Attack Strength) also has a higher Attack Strength than the opponent, an extra wound can be scored against the opponent.

After two Attack Rounds, if the opponent has not been defeated, a DWARF will enter the fight to try to even the sides up. The Dwarf will fight you while the other two fight and you must kill the Dwarf before you can return to aiding your ally.

DWARF	SKILL 6	STAMINA 6

If you survive this fight, turn to **293** if you aided the Sprite, or **335** if you aided the Pixie.

322

You follow the road to another junction. You can hear the voices of a crowd off to the left and you turn in this direction towards a bend in the road. Turn to **244**.

323

Whoever won the last fight is now the new champion. Resolve your battle with either the Ogre or the Barbarian:

	SKILL	STAMINA
OGRE	9	12
BARBARIAN	7	8

If you win, you will be given the prize money (15 Gold Pieces). The ruffian will ask whether you wish to remain as his new champion. But you have more important things to do. Turn to **263**.

You enter the hut and your eyes widen

324

You enter the hut and your eyes widen. The room inside is covered from floor to ceiling in trinkets, some piled up on shelves, some hanging from the ceiling, others leaning against the wall. The hut is lined with weapons, pottery, jewellery, domestic objects, magical items, and so on. Sitting cross-legged on the floor is a small bearded GNOME, who rubs his hands and greets you as you come in. In a squeaky voice he invites you to sit and barter with him. If you wish to barter, you will have to be prepared to exchange some of the items from your Equipment for some of his; if you have no items to barter with you may not sit down. If you would like to see what he has to offer, turn to **264**. If you cannot, or will not, barter, turn to **158**.

325

You leave the inn. In the morning light you can see that it is set almost on the riverside and is a short distance from the Harbour Bridge, the only crossing of the Jabaji. You cross the great river. On the far bank, there is a fork in the road. Will you turn left (turn to **132**) or right (turn to **198**)?

326

You cannot harm this great metal creature and your blow glances off it. In fact the only way of defeating it is to find its single weak spot. If you have been watching carefully, you may have picked up a clue as to where this weak spot is. Where will you try?

The right leg?	Turn to **265**
The left ankle?	Turn to **278**
The right thigh?	Turn to **35**
Somewhere else?	Turn to **93**

327

You hold your breath as the filthy liquid explodes from the shute all over your face. You are violently sick and you must deduct 3 *STAMINA* points. You climb out of the horrendous pile of sludge you are in and clean yourself off as best you can. Now you must try to find a way out. Will you:

Continue ahead, then first left, first right, first right, first left?	Turn to **10**
Continue ahead, then second right, first right and continue?	Turn to **298**
Continue ahead, then first right, first left, first right?	Turn to **77**

328

You soon arrive at another junction where you may either continue on towards a small group of dwellings (turn to **32**) or turn right (turn to **57**)

329

As they close in around you, you can feel small hands mauling your backpack. They are trying to reach inside it to see if you have anything worth stealing! *Test your Luck.* If you are Lucky, turn to **316**. If you are Unlucky, turn to **262**.

330

You struggle, but they hold you tight, forcing you over towards the pool. You strike one of them in the face, causing it to blink momentarily, but allowing you to see the small burning fireballs that these RED-EYES have for eyes. They shove you forwards into the pool. But the splash you were expecting does not occur. Turn to **270**.

331

You pay the innkeeper for the food. He disappears into a back room and comes back with a large plate of steaming grub. 'There ye go,' he laughs, 'And there's more if ye'll be needin' it.' You take the plate and sit down at a table to eat your meal. Gain 2 *STAMINA* points if this is your first meal today, or 1 *STAMINA* point if you have already eaten. As you are eating, a rough-looking sailor comes over and sits down with you. He tries to make conversation, but you are more intent on eating. Then he offers to buy you a mug of ale and you decide to accept. You finish your meal and sup the ale. Gain 1 *STAMINA* point for the drink. You start to talk to him and he asks of your quest. You tell him you are trying to find the spell which will open the North Gate. 'Oi'd loike ter 'elp yer,' he says, 'but ter foind the loin yer needs, ye'll 'ave ter *kill the undead,* an that ain't moi oidear of a fair foight. 'Ow about s'more ale?' Will you accept his offer and continue the conversation? (turn to **253**) or would you rather get some sleep (turn to **86**)?

332

He sizes you up, trying to decide how much you can afford. If your *SKILL* score is 8 or more, you look like a fairly powerful – and therefore wealthy – traveller, and he will ask for 5 Gold Pieces. If your *SKILL* is less than 8 he sees you as an ordinary visitor and he will ask for only 2 Gold Pieces. You may, if you wish, try to make yourself seem humble by *Testing your Luck*. If you are Lucky, he will let you bargain him down 1 Gold Piece on his price. If you wish to buy, pay him and turn to **203**. If you do not wish to pay his price, you must either leave (turn to **9**) or you may attack him, and try to steal his chain later (turn to **119**).

333

You soon become sleepy. But how far can you trust the old

man? Will you curl up on the floor and sleep for the night (turn to **21**) or will you stay awake, waiting for the guards and keeping an eye on your backpack (turn to **102**)?

334

Where will you kiss next: the forehead (turn to **314**); the right eye (turn to **2**); the left eye (turn to **163**); the left cheek (turn to **88**); the nose (turn to **296**); or the lips (turn to **231**)?

335

In a squeaky little voice, the Pixie thanks you for helping him. He asks if there is anything he could do in return. You tell him of your journey and ask whether he knows anything of the North Gate spell. Unfortunately he doesn't. But as you talk he does give you other information which may be useful. He tells you that you may learn more about the spell from a Priest who is very knowledgeable. You will meet him if you continue your journey and today he is trying to win converts to his faith in his chapel. He also warns you about the evils of the centre of Kharé – the dockland area – and advises that you watch your step, as Slaveseekers often prowl the area in the hope of kidnapping slaves as crew for their boats. A favourite ploy is to get a prospective slave senselessly drunk and then cart him off to their ship. You thank the Pixie for his advice and continue along the road. Turn to **153**. You may add 1 *LUCK* point for the warning.

He seems to be a fairly peaceful fellow

You follow him into his study, an elegant room lined floor to ceiling with books. You converse with him on the way and learn that he is a sage and scholar who now teaches local children. He seems to be a fairly peaceful fellow, quite out of character with the city he lives in. He explains he has had a good life and wishes to spend the rest of it doing what he can to help civilize the city. As it is apparent that he may be able to help you with your quest, you ask him if he knows anything of the spell needed to open the North Gate. 'Indeed, I know one line of the spell,' he says, 'and this I will gladly tell you if you can help me with a problem I am having.' You agree to help if you can. 'I have recently been trying to decipher some runes. I am working on an exercise but I am now stuck as I do not know which rune follows in the sequence. Which would you say should follow?' You have some knowledge of runes and study the problem carefully. Look at the sequence depicted in the illustration and choose the rune that you think should follow:

115   **255**   **274**   **72**

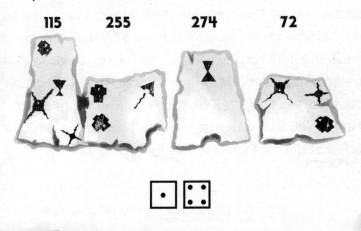

337

Deduct 5 *STAMINA* points. There is no such spell as this. Return to **1** and choose again.

338

Deduct 2 *STAMINA* points. You cast your spell into the pond and create the illusion of a small pile of gold next to the Gold Piece. The fish does not react. You cannot tell whether it is taken in by your illusion or not. Do you wish to try snatching the real Gold Piece (turn to **85**) or will you leave the pond and continue (turn to **28**)?

339

Deduct 1 *STAMINA* point. Do you have any beeswax with you? If not, you cannot use this spell and your double closes in with the first blow (lose 2 *STAMINA* points). If you have some beeswax, spread it on your weapon and cast your spell. You must now resolve the battle with your double, who has the same *SKILL* and *STAMINA* scores as you had before casting the spell and being struck. If your weapon has been magically enhanced, it will do double damage (i.e. 4 *STAMINA* points instead of the normal two). If you win, you must leave the hut (turn to **137**). The effect of the spell will last only for this fight.

340

There is no such spell as this. Return to **236** and choose again. If you did not expect VIK to be a spell, turn to **399**.

341

The Goblin walks over to the hut and steps inside. A minute later, it comes out and signals to you that there is no danger. Do you wish to enter the hut (turn to **27**) or will you now leave (turn to **137**)?

342

Deduct 1 *STAMINA* point. Do you have a Gold Piece with you? If not, your spell will not work. If you have a Gold Piece, you place it on your wrist and cast the spell. The coin radiates an invisible shield. During a battle, you may deduct 2 points from the creature's Attack Strength for the protection this shield gives you. You reach for your weapon. Turn to **243**. Remember that after the battle the shield and the Gold Piece vanish.

343

Deduct 1 *STAMINA* point. You cannot use this spell as you do not have the Jewel-Studded Medallion it requires. Turn to **179**.

344

Deduct 5 *STAMINA* points. There is no such spell as this. Return to **254** and choose again.

345

Deduct 1 *STAMINA* point. You cast the spell but nothing happens. You may not use this spell as you do not have the Staff of Oak Sapling it requires. The Chainmaker steps in and lashes you with his chain. Deduct 2 *STAMINA* points. Return to **119**, draw your weapon and fight the Chainmaker.

346

Deduct 1 *STAMINA* point. You cannot use this spell as you do not have the Yellow Powder it requires. Return to **108** and make another choice.

347

Deduct 5 *STAMINA* points. There is no such spell as this. Return to **43** and choose your next course of action.

348

Deduct 1 *STAMINA* point. You cannot use this spell as you do not have the Stone Dust it requires. However, you believe the statue has now been petrified and you step forwards. Turn to **8**.

349

Deduct 1 *STAMINA* point. Do you have a Gold-Backed Mirror with you? If not, you may not cast this spell – draw your weapon and turn to **192**. If you have a Gold-Backed Mirror, you may draw it out from your pack and cast the spell on it. Focusing it on the creatures, their images reflect in the mirror and exact replicas form in front of you. The original creatures are taken aback, and you command your replicas to attack. Although you may not have known it, these creatures are RED-EYES. Their eyes are closed, but when they open their eyelids, jets of flame shoot from them to burn anything in their path. So the battle is short but deadly: as each Red-Eye gazes at, and is gazed upon by, his opponent, it falls to the ground, scorched and very dead. If they stole any Gold you may recover it and continue your journey. Turn to **89**.

350

'You offer me a *Goblin*!' says the Gnome, incredulously. 'What use will I have for a Goblin?' Your creation is worthless to him. Do you now wish to command the Goblin to attack (turn to **403**) or will you tell it to disappear and settle down to barter with the Gnome (return to **264**)?

351

Deduct 1 *STAMINA* point. Do you have any grains of sand with you? If not, return to **213**. If you do have any grains of sand, you may sprinkle these into the water and cast your spell. The pond will turn into a pool of quicksand. The little fish will undoubtedly die in the sludge, but you will be able to grab the Gold Piece before it sinks. Take the Gold if you wish and press onwards (turn to **28**). Remember to cross the sand you have used off your Equipment List.

352

You climb from the ring and Vik makes his way over to you. The two of you chat for some time. You tell him of your adventures in the Shamutanti Hills and the return of Glandragor's axe. You ask him whether he knows anything of the spell lines needed to open the North Gate and he nods. How many spell lines do you have already:

None	Turn to **380**
One	Turn to **409**
Two	Turn to **372**

353

Deduct 4 *STAMINA* points. You cast the spell and an invisible wall forms in front of you. This would be very useful if you were being attacked, but is totally inappropriate to your present predicament. You have wasted your *STAMINA*. Turn to **154**.

354

Deduct 1 *STAMINA* point. Do you have a Giant's tooth with you? If not, this spell will not work and you will have to face the creatures with your weapon. Turn to **192**. If you have a Giant's tooth, you may drop it on the ground and cast your spell. A haze forms around the tooth from which steps a towering Giant. You command it to attack the creatures and it steps towards them. But your Giant has little chance against these RED-EYES. They merely have to blink at it and, as soon as their eyes open, streams of fire shoot towards your creation. The Giant puts up a valiant fight, but is no match for them. However, the delay does allow you to nip off through the back streets. After the Red-Eyes have killed your Giant, they follow in hot pursuit. Turn to **41**.

355

Deduct 5 *STAMINA* points. There is no such spell as this and nothing happens as you clumsily try to cast it. Your host watches your pitiful conjurations and is getting impatient. You tell him to continue, and you drink from the mug. Turn to **236**.

356

Deduct 2 *STAMINA* points. As your double advances, you cast your spell and create a small pile of illusionary treasure. Your opponent is not in the least interested and starts the attack. You now have no other opportunity to cast spells. Resolve this battle. If you win, leave the hut and turn to **137**. Remember your double has the same *SKILL* and *STAMINA* as you had before casting the spell.

357

Deduct 1 *STAMINA* point. You do not have the Holy Water you need to cast this spell, so it does not work. As you are trying to make it work, the body parts close in and attack you. Deduct 3 *STAMINA* points. Return to **11** and choose again.

358

Deduct 1 *STAMINA* point. Do you have any sand with you? If not, you may not use this spell and will have to fight the Statue – turn to **299**. If you have some sand, you may throw it to the ground beneath the Statue's feet and cast your spell onto it. As the spell takes effect, the ground around the Statue's feet begins to bubble. The great giant begins to lose its balance as the spell creates a pool of quicksand beneath it! Uncertain of its footing, it holds its position and slowly sinks into the ground. When it has disappeared, you may choose your path forwards. Will you head along the left fork out of the cityport (turn to **104**) or take the road to the right towards the Gambling Halls of Vlada (turn to **56**)? Remember to cross the sand you have used off your Equipment List.

359

Do you have any Goblin teeth with you? If so, you may place one on the ground and cast your spell on it (if not, lose 1 *STAMINA* and return to **153** to make another choice). Deduct 1 *STAMINA* as you cast the spell on the tooth. A Goblin materializes in front of you. Do you want to send the Goblin to take a look at the statue (turn to **423**) or to look in the hut (turn to **341**)?

360

Deduct 2 *STAMINA* points. You cast your spell to detect the presence of any magical traps that may be a danger to you. There is no magic being used. If you wish to deal with the Gnome, return to **264**. If you would prefer to leave, turn to **158**.

361

Deduct 5 *STAMINA* points. There is no such spell as this. Return to **34** and make another choice.

362

There is no such spell as this. Turn to **323** and fight your battle. If you were not expecting this to be a spell, turn to **436**.

363

Deduct 2 *STAMINA* points. You cast your spell and create an illusionary mound of treasure in the road, promising this to the creatures. They scoff haughtily at you and one shouts out: 'You feeble-minded barnacle! Our eyes may be closed, but we are not blind. Your riches are naught but an illusion! Let's have this dimwit, friends!' They move towards you. You draw your weapon. Turn to **192**.

364

Deduct 5 *STAMINA* points. There is no such spell as this. You must fight your double with your weapon. Resolve the battle – remember your double has the same *SKILL* and *STAMINA* as you had before casting the spell – and leave the hut if you win. Turn to **137**.

These teeth will turn into fully-formed Goblins

365

Do you have any Goblin teeth? If not, you may not use this spell – deduct 1 *STAMINA* point and turn to **118**. If you have some Goblin teeth, you may drop as many as you want on the floor and cast your spell on them. Deduct 1 *STAMINA* point for each tooth you use. Within moments, these teeth will turn into fully formed Goblins and you may command them to help you fight the winged creatures. Each Goblin will have 5 *SKILL* and 5 *STAMINA* points. Turn to **118** and fight the tormenting creatures. They will always attack you and the beggar, but you may choose which of your Goblins are attacking which creature (before you roll for Attack Strength). If a Goblin's Attack Strength is higher than that of the creature it is attacking, it will inflict a wound as normal. After the battle, any remaining Goblins will disappear.

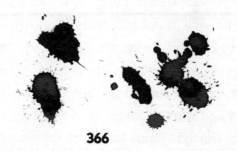

366

Deduct 2 *STAMINA* points. You cast your spell. Behind Vangorn the door opens into the street. He does not flinch. Turn to **13**.

367

Deduct 1 *STAMINA* point. Do you have a Black Facemask with you? If not, this spell will not work and you will have to fight them with your weapon (turn to **192**). If you have a Black Facemask, you may hold it up to your face and cast the spell. The creatures surrounding you back away in fear, allowing you to continue. Turn to **135**.

368

You cast your spell on to the teeth and each forms into a Goblin, under your control. You send the Goblins running after the Orclings. But unfortunately, they have had too much of a head start on the Goblins and you cannot recover any of your possessions. You must continue up the road. Turn to **61**.

369

Deduct 1 *STAMINA* point. Do you have a Bamboo Flute with you? If not you cannot make this spell work – return to **234** and resolve the fight. If you have a Bamboo Flute, you may pull it out, play a tune and cast the spell. Whichever of the contestants you aim the spell at will stop fighting and start to dance uncontrollably. But when this happens the fight stops and all eyes turn angrily towards you for tampering with the contest. Someone in the crowd grabs your Flute and breaks it while the others push you out of the crowd. You will have to leave. Turn to **263**.

370

Deduct 1 *STAMINA* point. Do you have any beeswax with you? If not, you cannot use this spell and must deduct another 2 *STAMINA* points as the Chainmaker's chain flays your back – return to **119** and draw your weapon to fight him. If you have beeswax, you may rub it quickly on your weapon and cast the spell on it. This spell will make your weapon razor-sharp. Each time you inflict a wound on the Chainmaker, you may deduct 4 *STAMINA* points instead of the usual 2. Return to **119** and fight him.

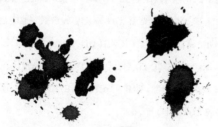

371

Deduct 4 *STAMINA* points. Pointing your finger at the door, you unleash a flashing blast of lightning. The scorched door flies open, allowing you and the old man to escape. You both run off down the road to a junction ahead. The old man is surprisingly fast for his age and he reaches the junction before you. Turn to **81**.

372

He advises you to carry straight on until you reach the port. You thank him and continue. Turn to **263**.

373

Deduct 4 *STAMINA* points. You cast the spell and an invisible wall forms in the air between you and the Living Corpse. The creature's various parts fly into the wall and bounce off. But the spell has a limited range and it is not long before they have flown around your defence and once again threaten you. Return to **11** and make another choice.

374

Deduct 1 *STAMINA* point. Do you have a Gold Piece with you? If not, this spell will not work – turn to **468**. If you have a coin, you may place it on your wrist and cast your spell. An invisible shield will form on your arm. It will stay in place as long as you are in this shrine and will aid you in any battles you may have, but then it (and the Gold Piece) will vanish. Now turn to **468**.

375

Deduct 4 *STAMINA* points. You cast your spell into the pond, aimed at the fish. But the little creature quickly darts out of the way and the spell hits a little snail which was grazing on a rock beneath the fish. You may now control the snail – but this will be of little use to you! Do you want to grab the Gold Piece (turn to **85**) or leave the pond (turn to **28**)?

376

Deduct 1 *STAMINA* point. Do you have any medicinal potions or Blimberry juice with you? If not, the spell will have no effect and the poison will take its toll – you will have come to the end of this adventure. If you have such a potion, you can drink it quickly and cast the spell on yourself. The potion will counteract the poison. You will rapidly recover your strength – you may restore your *STAMINA* to its *Initial* level. The man watches as you do this. When you have fully recovered, you may leave the house. Turn to **223**.

377

Deduct 2 *STAMINA* points. You cast your spell and you may now enter the crypt in safety. Turn to **249**. You may wish to take something out of your pack before you enter. If you want to do this, turn to **7**.

378

Deduct 1 *STAMINA* point. Do you have a vial of glue? If not, the spell will not work and the creature bites your ankle (lose 2 *STAMINA* points) – return to **95** and fight the creature. If you have some glue, you may throw it at the Bristle Beast and cast your spell. The creature becomes stuck to the ground and it is now an easy matter for you to advance and finish it off. Turn to **14**.

WIN 5 GOLD PIECES

379

Deduct 5 *STAMINA* points. There is no such spell as this and nothing happens when you cast it. Return to **98** and make another choice.

380

Vik tells you how to reach the keeper of one of the spell lines. You may follow his directions back towards the South Gate until you reach the road where he says you will find a keeper (turn to **61**) or you may continue the way you were heading (turn to **263**).

381

Deduct 2 *STAMINA* points. You cast the spell on the lock of the gate. The tumblers turn and two bolts on the inside free the door. You push the gate open and slide inside. There is no one around and you survey the area. Your first cover is a building just inside the wall and you nip over to it. It is a stone building with barred windows. The inside is bare apart from a wooden bench on which an old man is sitting. Do you wish to enter the building and greet the man (turn to **169**) or leave and continue onwards (turn to **218**)?

382

Deduct 1 *STAMINA* point. Do you have a Gold-Backed Mirror with you? If not, this spell will not work and they close in as you try in vain to defend yourself – you will have to draw your weapon (turn to **192**). If you have a Gold-Backed Mirror, you pull it quickly out of your pack, face it towards the group and cast your spell. The reflection creates a group of identical creatures and the two groups face each other, ready to fight. Meanwhile, you may escape from the scene – turn to **135**.

383

Deduct 4 *STAMINA* points. You cast your spell and an invisible wall forms between the two of you. The Murderer releases his arrow and it bounces off your shielding wall. 'A Sorcerer!' says Vangorn. 'I have no quarrel with Sorcerers. You may leave, stranger.' He lowers his bow and steps away from the door to allow you to leave. Turn to **46**.

384

Deduct 2 *STAMINA* points. You cast your spell and five images of yourself form around you. You hope the great Statue will be confused, but alas the creature is not taken in by your illusion and it swipes at you. The tip of its hand catches you and knocks you to the ground – deduct 1 *STAMINA* point's worth of damage. You grab for your weapon. Turn to **299**.

385

Deduct 2 *STAMINA* points. You cast the spell over your opponent, whose attack slows down. Your double appears listless and cannot concentrate on the fight. Resolve the battle, but during this fight deduct 3 points from your double's *SKILL*. Remember your double has the same *SKILL* (now 3 less) and *STAMINA* as you had before casting the spell. If you win this fight, leave the hut (turn to **137**).

386

Do you have any Goblin teeth with you? If not, you may not cast this spell – return to **264** and choose again, but deduct 1 *STAMINA* point for your unsuccessful attempt. If you have some Goblin teeth, you may drop one on the ground and cast your spell on it. Deduct 1 *STAMINA* point. Your spell causes the tooth to form into an ugly Goblin, who now stands before you waiting for your instructions. Will you tell it to attack the Gnome (turn to **403**) or will you offer it for barter against the Gnome's wares (turn to **350**)?

387

Deduct 1 *STAMINA* point. You cast the spell but nothing happens. You cannot use it as you do not have the Orb of Crystal it requires. You are embarrassed at your pathetic attempts at sorcery and drink your ale, smiling sheepishly at your host. Turn to **236**.

388

Deduct 1 *STAMINA* point. Do you have a Giant's tooth? If not, you have wasted your *STAMINA* as the spell will not work – turn to **154**. If you have a Giant's tooth, you manage to throw it on the ground and cast your spell on it. A smoky vapour spurts from the ground around the tooth and, as it clears, a large, brutish Giant stands before you. You command it to break you free from the chains and it does so easily, disappearing when the task is completed. You may now leave the hut. Turn to **9**.

389

Deduct 1 *STAMINA* point. Do you have a Gold Piece with you? If not, this spell will not work (return to **310** and choose your next move). If you have a Gold Piece, you may place this on your wrist and cast your spell on it. An invisible shield, attached to your arm, will form and this will be a useful defence in your fight. Turn to **118** and fight the creatures, but this shield will protect you by allowing you to deduct 2 points from the Attack Strength of any creature attacking you. After the battle, the shield – and your Gold Piece – will disappear.

390

Deduct 2 *STAMINA* points. You cast your spell and you will be protected from any traps for a short period. You may now either enter the crypt (turn to **249**) or reach into your pack to pull out anything that may be useful (turn to **7**).

391

Deduct 1 *STAMINA* point. Do you have a pair of nose plugs? If so, put them on straight away. You cast your spell towards the fight. A horrendous stench swells up and hangs in the air. The crowd cough and hold their breaths as they run away from the scene and the fight stops immediately. If you do not have the nose plugs, the smell affects you, making you feel ill and causing 3 *STAMINA* points' worth of damage. You may now continue along the road. Turn to **153**.

392

You remember the words of Glandragor: 'If you have any problems in Kharé just call for Vik, a friend of mine who has power and influence.' You shout out his name several times, asking for help. Some time later a face appears at the opening at the ceiling and snarls, 'Who asked for Vik?' You identify yourself and the face disappears, to return later with what must be the captain of the ship. You tell him your story. 'I must apologize to you,' says the captain, 'for my over-zealous crew. They could not have known that we had a friend in common. For Vik is indeed my friend. In fact I owe my life to him: he rescued me from the clutches of the Shield Maidens of Lumle. Do not fear for your freedom.' A rope ladder drops into the hold and you are allowed to climb on to the ship's deck. You leave hastily. Turn to **487**.

393

Deduct 2 *STAMINA* points. You cast your spell over the shambling creature and its already slow movements become even slower. You may now draw your weapon and fight it:

SLIME EATER   *SKILL 7*   *STAMINA 11*

While under your spell, for the first four Attack Rounds, it will fight you with a *SKILL* of 4. After this, its movements and its *SKILL* will return to normal. If you defeat the creature, turn to **196**.

394

Deduct 1 *STAMINA* point. You cannot cast this spell as you do not have the Staff of Oak Sapling which it requires. Turn to **55**.

395

Deduct 2 *STAMINA* points. You cast your spell and, as it takes effect, you can sense the areas of danger ahead. Certainly the dark circle ahead of you is a danger and you should avoid it. The crypt itself can also be a danger and if you enter you should make sure you carry a special weapon. Your *safest* path is to leave the crypt, but this may not be your *best* choice. If you wish to leave, turn to **16**. If you wish to enter, turn to **249**. If you wish to take something from your pack before you enter, turn to **7**.

396

Deduct 5 *STAMINA* points. There is no such spell as this. The Orclings have run off while you have been trying in vain to cast it. Turn to **61**.

397

You mumble a curse as they advance. Your sword is a less useful weapon than a hammer or an axe would be in this situation, and the thought puts you in mind of Glandragor's Tavern. What was it he told you? If you have any problems in Kharé just call for Vik ...' As you back away from the group, you decide it may be worth a try. You tell them they may not harm you, as you are a friend of Vik's. At the mention of the name, they stop. Whispers pass among them: 'A friend of Vik's ... Then we daren't touch this stranger ... What if it's a bluff? ... Can we risk it? ...' Eventually, they step aside to let you pass and you can continue. Turn to **135**.

398

Deduct 5 *STAMINA* points. There is no such spell as this. Return to **43** and choose your next course of action.

You remember the words of kind Glandragor in Birritanti. If only his friend Vik were here to help you! But in your agony, you have been mumbling out loud and at the mention of Vik's name, Vangorn rushes forwards and holds up your head. 'Do you know Vik?' he asks. You nod. He rushes off to his kitchen and comes bustling back with a tiny cup with some liquid in it. He forces it between your lips and there is little you can do to stop him. The pain is overwhelming and you pass out. Some time later you regain consciousness. You blink awake and find that Vangorn has seated you in a chair and is watching you attentively. He smiles as you come round and asks you how you know of Vik. You tell him the story of Glandragor's axe. 'Vik,' he tells you, 'is my brother. It is weeks since I have seen him, but I love him dearly. Any friend of Vik's is a friend of mine.' He asks you how you feel and whether you would like another sip of the antidote he has given you. But you are recovering fast. He apologizes continually for poisoning you. You wish to leave but ask whether he can be of any help in your quest. He gives you 5 Gold Pieces and a Black Facemask which may be useful for your spells. He also gives you a word of advice: 'If you come across the Bronze Statue, study it carefully. It has a single weakness only.' You thank him and leave. Add 2 *LUCK* points for your discovery and turn to **46**.

400

Deduct 1 *STAMINA* point. You cannot use this spell as you do not have the Jewel of Gold it requires. Return to **98** and make another choice.

401

Deduct 1 *STAMINA* point. Do you have a skullcap? If not, you cannot cast this spell – turn to **55**. If you have a skullcap, you place it on your head, cast your spell and remain on your guard, waiting for any telepathic messages. You begin to pick up intelligent thoughts coming from the statue! It is a living creature and is looking on you as its next meal! You back away from it around the hut. When you are out of sight, you may run off, heading back towards the road. Turn to **137**.

402

There is no such spell as this. Return to **312** and choose again. If you did not expect this to be a spell, turn to **392**.

403

The Goblin snarls at the Gnome and steps forwards to attack. 'Hah!' sneers the Barterer. 'So you think this little fellow will be more than a match for me, eh? Well think again, stranger!' He reaches behind him, takes the stopper off a small vial of liquid, and tosses it over the Goblin. In a second, the Goblin is frozen in position as a statue. 'Do you wish to see more of my power?' asks the little creature. You choose to leave immediately. Turn to **158**.

404

Deduct 1 *STAMINA* point. You cannot use this spell as you do not have the Bracelet of Bone it requires. As you fumble with the spell, the Orclings run off and you will never be able to catch them now. Turn to **61**.

405

Deduct 1 *STAMINA* point. Do you have any medicinal potions or Blimberry juice with you? If not, this spell will come to nothing. If you have a medicinal potion, you may drink it quickly and cast your spell. The effect is invigorating. You may restore your *STAMINA* to its *Initial* level. But now you must resolve your fight. Turn to **323**. Remember you have used up your potion.

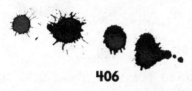

406

Deduct 1 *STAMINA* point. You are not able to use this spell as you do not have the Potion of Fire Water it requires. The pain in your stomach becomes more acute and you soon lose consciousness. Vangorn the Murderer has claimed another victim ...

407

Deduct 1 *STAMINA* point and cast your spell. As you do so, a horrendous stench wafts through the air. The smell is so bad that it will make you ill (causing 3 *STAMINA* points' worth of damage) unless you have a pair of nose plugs which will protect you. The smell will keep your enemies at bay for some time while you nip off through the back streets, but as the spell wears off, they will follow you in hot pursuit. Turn to **41**.

408

Deduct 1 *STAMINA* point. You cannot use this spell without the Galehorn it requires. Return to **1** and choose again.

409

Vik advises you to press on ahead and, at your first opportunity, turn left. If you turn either first or second right – he is not sure which – you should find someone who knows one of the lines. You thank him and continue. Turn to **263**.

410

Deduct 2 *STAMINA* points. You cast your spell over both creatures and they begin to get sluggish. Their movements slow down and the fight fizzles out as they both realize magic is in the air. They, and the rest of the crowd, begin to look around to see who has spoiled the fun. You decide to leave smartly. Turn to **153**.

411

Deduct 1 *STAMINA* point. Do you have a Giant's tooth with you? If not, you cannot get this spell to work and while you are trying, the Statue knocks you over – lose 1 *STAMINA* point of damage and turn to **299**. If you have a Giant's tooth, you can throw it on the ground and cast your spell on it to create a stocky Giant who will fight the Statue for you. Resolve the battle:

	SKILL	STAMINA
BRONZE STATUE	10	15
GIANT	8	9

If your Giant wins, it will disappear. You may then choose your next path: either out of Kharé (turn to **104**) or into the Gambling Halls (turn to **56**). If your Giant loses, you will have to finish the fight off yourself, but when you strike your first blow, turn to **326**.

WIN 20 GOLD PIECES

This is a Sulphur Ghost, whose poisonous fumes are suffocating you!

412

You recite your spell and wait. A tingle runs down your back as a creaking noise comes from the gate. But rather than seeing the gate open in front of you, you see a ghost-like puff of smoke come from a wooden box high up on the frame. It skips about in the air like a puppet and you are transfixed watching it. Suddenly it shoots down towards you and, before you can react, it has engulfed you! You cough and sweat, panicking as you realize that this is a SULPHUR GHOST, whose poisonous fumes are suffocating you! As you were warned, the North Gate of Kharé has its own defences, and the uninitiated attempt to open it only at the risk of their own lives. Yours has now been lost ...

413

Deduct 1 *STAMINA* point. You may not use this spell as you do not have the Orb of Crystal it requires. Do you now wish to take a closer look at the statue (turn to **8**) or enter the hut (turn to **27**)?

414

Deduct 2 *STAMINA* points. You cast your spell and wait for signs of how you may most safely proceed. Drinking the ale is evidently not a wise move, but your host is bending over you, waiting for you to drink. In a flash, you fling the mug of ale into his face and race for the door. You reach the door before he knows what has happened. Turn to **46**.

415

Deduct 5 *STAMINA* points. There is no such spell as this. Turn to **154**.

416

Deduct 1 *STAMINA* point. Do you have a Sun Jewel with you? If not, you may not cast this spell – return to **234** and resolve the fight. If you have a Sun Jewel, you may cast your spell on it. The Jewel will glow intensely and you may use it to aid your favoured fighter. The spell will last for the first 3 Attack Rounds. During the first three rounds, if your fighter's opponent inflicts any wounds on your fighter, you may shine the jewel in his eyes. The blinding effect will reduce the damage to 1 *STAMINA* point instead of the normal two. Remember this will only work during the first three Attack Rounds; after this the fighting will be as normal. Now return to **234** and resolve the fight.

417

Deduct 2 *STAMINA* points. You cast your spell over the FLAYER and it stops. It turns away from you and wanders aimlessly around the room, bumping into things. While it is in this confused state, you may take the box under the table. Turn to **29**.

418

Deduct 1 *STAMINA* point. Do you have a skullcap with you? If not, your spell will not work. If you have a skullcap, you may place it on your head and cast the spell. As it takes effect, you wait to receive telepathic messages from any creatures which may be near by. You receive no such messages. There are no living creatures in the vicinity. Will you now walk up to the door (turn to **288**) or jump over the circle (turn to **258**)?

419

Deduct 1 *STAMINA* point. Do you have a medicinal potion or Blimberry juice with you? If not, you cannot use this spell (return to **264**) and choose again. If so, you may drink the potion and cast your spell. As the magic takes effect, you begin to feel invigorated – a surge of strength passes through you. You may restore your *STAMINA* to its *Initial* level. Now return to **264** and arrange your deal with the Gnome. Remember you have used up your potion.

420

Deduct 1 *STAMINA* point. Do you have a skullcap with you? If not, you cannot make this spell work (return to **108** and make another choice). If you have a skullcap, you may place it on your head and cast your spell. You probe the mind of the firemaster outside the hut. 'Will this traveller fall into my trap?' he is thinking. It seems that he expects you to try to enter the fire. Do you wish to step into the flames (turn to **130**) or will you leave this place (turn to **137**)?

421

You recite your spell and wait. A tingle runs down your back as a creaking noise comes from the gate. But rather than seeing the gate open in front of you, you see a ghost-like puff of smoke come from a wooden box high up on the frame. It skips about in the air like a puppet and you are transfixed watching it. Suddenly it shoots down towards you and, before you can react, it has engulfed you! You cough and sweat, panicking as you realize that this is a SULPHUR GHOST, whose poisonous fumes are suffocating you! As you were warned, the North Gate of Kharé has its own defences, and the uninitiated attempt to open it only at the risk of their own lives. Yours has now been lost . . .

422

Deduct 1 *STAMINA* point. Do you have any sand with you? If not, your spell will not work – draw your weapon and turn to **192**. If you have some sand, you may throw it to the ground around their feet and cast your spell on it. The ground begins to bubble as the quicksand you have created forms beneath the creatures. They lose their balance and fall over, become trapped and sink. They call out for help but within moments they have disappeared. Unfortunately, so has any Gold they stole. You may now continue by turning to **89**. Remember you have now used up one of the portions of sand you may have found.

423

Your Goblin steps up to the Statue. A loud barking noise behind you makes you swing round. But it was only a dog who now runs off down the road barking at every creature it passes. You turn back to the Statue and gasp as you see your Goblin lying dead in front of the Statue, which has not moved at all! Do you want to take a closer look at the Statue (turn to **8**), look inside the hut (turn to **27**) or leave quickly (turn to **137**)?

424

Deduct 5 *STAMINA* points. There is no such spell as this. Return to **317** and make another choice.

425

Deduct 1 *STAMINA* point. You cast the spell but nothing happens. You may not use this spell as you do not have the Jewel of Gold it requires. Turn to **323** and resolve your battle.

426

Do you have any teeth from Goblins? If not, deduct 1 *STAMINA* point, as your spell will not work without them, and continue up the road (turn to **61**). If you do have Goblin teeth, throw any number you wish onto the ground and cast your spell. Deduct as many *STAMINA* points as the number of teeth you use and turn to **368**.

427

Deduct 1 *STAMINA* point. Do you have a Bamboo Flute with you? If not, you cannot use this spell and, as you try to work it, the creature closes in and swipes at you, knocking you over for 2 *STAMINA* points of damage – return to **77** and conduct the battle. If you have a Bamboo Flute, you may cast your spell over the Slime Eater and play. The tune stops the bulky creature and it cocks its head to one side. Suddenly it leaps from the water, howling loudly and, as it lands, it starts what must be the nearest thing to a dance that a Slime Eater can perform! You can back off now while it is unable to attack you. Turn to **196**.

428

Deduct 5 *STAMINA* points. There is no such spell as this. Return to **26** and make another choice.

429

Deduct 4 *STAMINA* points. You cast the spell and a powerful force-field surrounds you. As long as this is in operation, no harm can befall you. You approach the Statue. Nothing happens. You look into the hut. It is empty apart from the debris on the floor. No one is around. The spell eventually wears off. Will you enter the hut (turn to **27**), approach the Statue to take the locket (turn to **8**) or leave (turn to **137**)?

430

Deduct 2 *STAMINA* points. You cast the spell and wait for it to take effect. The pain in your stomach increases until it is unbearable and you pass out. You will never awaken. Your spell would have protected you from magic, but this poison is not magical at all. You have failed in your mission . . .

431

Deduct 2 *STAMINA* points. You cast your spell. As long as you are inside the Shrine of Courga, you are protected from magic spells. Turn to **468**.

WIN 10 GOLD PIECES

432

Deduct 2 *STAMINA* points. You cast your spell at the door and can hear the tumblers in the lock clicking. Giving the door a push, it swings open and you can escape. The old man leaves with you, thanks you for helping him escape, and hurries off down the road ahead of you. You soon reach a junction. Turn to **81**.

433

Deduct 2 *STAMINA* points. You cast your spell. While it is working, you are protected from any magical traps. Now turn to **118** and fight the creatures. This spell will last for the duration of the fight.

434

Deduct 4 *STAMINA* points. You cast your spell and hold your hands towards the group. Two small fireballs form in the palms of your hands and you fling these at the creatures. One of the RED-EYES you are facing opens his eyes and a jet of fire shoots forward to intercept your fireballs. The clash sends your fireballs bouncing back towards you and you must leap out of the way to avoid them. You land under the monument in the pool beneath it – but the splash you were expecting does not occur. Turn to **270**.

435

Deduct 2 *STAMINA* points. You cast your spell and five identical images form around you to confuse the creature. But this illusion will only be effective against the creature's *Head* as the other body parts do not have an intelligence of their own. Return to **11** and resolve your fight. If in any Attack Round the Corpse's Head rolls a higher Attack Strength than you, roll one die. If you roll 1–5, the Head has attacked one of the images you have created. If you roll a 6, the Head has selected the real you and you must take normal damage.

436

From your corner, you overhear a voice in the crowd: 'Vik! Vik, my friend! How goes it with you?' You look over and see two people greeting each other. You call out to Vik, telling him you are a friend of Glandragor's. At this name, a smile breaks out over Vik's face. He says he will wait for you after the fight and wishes you luck. Add 2 *LUCK* for meeting him. Return to **82** and choose again. If you survive the fight, turn afterwards to **352** if you wish to talk to Vik.

437

Deduct 5 *STAMINA* points. There is no such spell as this. Return to **95** and either fight the creature or choose another spell.

438

Deduct 2 *STAMINA* points. You cast your spell and create a small pile of treasure on the ground by your feet. You call up to the opening above you and a face appears. A member of the crew growls at you and asks what you want. A greedy smile spreads over his face as you show him the treasure. He looks around and lowers a rope ladder to allow you to climb up. When you reach the top you hand him the false riches and quickly leave the ship. Turn to **487**.

439

Deduct 1 *STAMINA* point. You cannot use this spell as you do not have the Ring of Green Metal it requires. Return to **26** and make another choice.

440

Deduct 5 *STAMINA* points. There is no such spell as this. Return to **119** draw your weapon and fight the Chainmaker.

441

Deduct 1 *STAMINA* point. Do you have any small pebbles with you? If not, you try in vain to cast your spell but nothing happens and the dismembered body flies around you inflicting 2 *STAMINA* points' worth of damage. If you have small pebbles, you may cast this spell over them. The spell will make each pebble explode on impact and disable – to the extent of 1 *STAMINA* point of damage – any part of the body that you hit. You may activate as many pebbles as you wish and throw each at a body part. To determine whether it hits or not, throw two dice. If the number you roll is *equal to* or *less than* your *SKILL*, then this pebble hits and damages that part of the corpse's body. If you roll *higher than* your *SKILL*, the pebble misses. Repeat this for each pebble you throw – and you may choose your target. Return to **11** and resolve your battle. You may use as many of your exploding pebbles as you wish but you must fight any body parts that remain after you have thrown your pebbles.

442

Deduct 1 *STAMINA* point. Do you have any Blimberry juice or a medicinal potion with you? If not, the spell will not work. If so, you may drink it down and cast your spell. Your strength will grow and your wounds heal as the magic takes effect. You may restore your *STAMINA* to its *Initial* level. Whether or not the spell has worked, you must now either walk up to the door (turn to **288**) or jump over the circle (turn to **258**). Remember you have used up your potion.

443

Deduct 2 *STAMINA* points. You cast your spell and wait to see what effect it will have on the creature (as you know, this spell has unpredictable effects). The Bristle Beast stops dead in its tracks and looks at you. It moves a little sluggishly and seems to be deciding what to do next. Suddenly it leaps at you and knocks you over (lose 1 *STAMINA* point). But instead of pursuing the fight, it starts to run around in circles! Return to **95** and either fight the creature or choose another spell. If you decide to fight, you may deduct 1 *SKILL* point from it, as it is in this confused state.

444

You place the skullcap on your head and cast the spell. You concentrate on your host's mind and momentary thoughts pass through your own. One thing is certain; he wants you to drink the drink as it is drugged in some way. You may either drink the ale as he wishes (turn to **236**) or make an excuse and stand to leave (turn to **173**).

445

Deduct 2 *STAMINA* points. You cast your spell on to the table and a small pile of gold materializes. The creature's eyes fix on this for a few moments, then it looks at you. From its manner, it appears to have seen through your illusion and is angry that you should have tried such a trick. It advances and your hand feels for your weapon. Turn to **243**.

446

Deduct 4 *STAMINA* points. You cast your spell and wait for an indication of a safe choice which will recover any gold they may have stolen. Nothing happens. Are these creatures blocking your spell? Or is it merely that there *is* no safe course of action? The creatures advance. You draw your weapon. Turn to **192**.

447

Deduct 1 *STAMINA* point. This spell will not work as you do not have the Staff of Oak Sapling it requires. Return to **98** and make another choice.

448

Deduct 1 *STAMINA* point. Do you have a skullcap with you? If not, your spell will not work and the Orclings disappear as you try to make it work (continue by turning to **61**). If you have a skullcap, you place it on your head and cast the spell. You are able telepathically to tune into each of the Orclings. They are all running different ways, but you can select the one who has stolen your most valuable possession and follow it. You will eventually catch up with it and force it to hand back your property. Then you may return and continue your journey (turn to **61**).

449

Deduct 1 *STAMINA* point. Do you have any grains of sand with you? If not, this spell will not work and as you try in vain to cast it, the Chainmaker lashes you with his chain for 2 *STAMINA* points' worth of damage – return to **119**, draw your weapon and fight. If you have grains of sand with you, you may cast these down at the feet of the Chainmaker and cast your spell over them. The ground begins to bubble and boil and the Chainmaker loses his balance. He is standing on a pool of quicksand and is sinking slowly into it! He takes off his jacket and spreads it out over the quicksand, trying to use it as a break to slow his sinking. You step over and pull the jacket away and he disappears under the surface. Turn to **195**. You have used all your sand and you may only use this spell again if you have another supply of sand.

450

Deduct 1 *STAMINA* point. Do you have a Gold Piece? If not, you may not use this spell and as you try to make it work, the body inflicts 2 *STAMINA* points' worth of damage. If you have a Gold Piece you may place it on your wrist and cast your spell on it. It will form into an invisible shield which will help you in your fight. Return to **11** and fight the body, but you may deduct 2 points from each body part's Attack Strength because of the magical shield you are using. The shield – and the Gold Piece, of course – will vanish after the fight.

451

Deduct 1 *STAMINA* point. Do you have a Giant's tooth? If not, this spell will not work – turn to **323** and resolve your battle. If you have a Giant's tooth, you may cast your spell on it and create a magical Giant. The crowd gasps as the Giant appears and you explain to the ruffian that this Giant is your champion and he will fight in your place. Turn to **323** and resolve the fight between the champion and your Giant:

GIANT   *SKILL 8*   *STAMINA 9*

If your Giant wins, you may collect the prize money on his behalf.

452

Deduct 2 *STAMINA* points. You cast your spell and immediately your body starts to grow, until you are almost Giant-sized. Unfortunately you will not now be able to fit through the crypt doorway! You may either leave the place (turn to **16**) or wait for the spell to wear off before you enter (turn to **249**).

453

Deduct 2 *STAMINA* points. You cast the spell around yourself and step into the flames. You feel nothing. You open up the chest in the middle of the fire and find 10 Silver Pieces and a Silver Mirror. You grab these and step out of the flames. You look at your treasures and, before your eyes, the objects turn from silver to gold! You have found 10 Gold Pieces and an elegant Gold-Backed Mirror. You quickly hide them in your pack as a voice calls from outside: 'Well, what do you think?' You remember that you are supposed to be considering the fire! You leave the hut telling him you are not interested, thank him for the demonstration, and walk on down the road. Turn to **137**.

454

Deduct 5 *STAMINA* points. There is no such spell as this, and the Statue is almost on you. Draw your weapon and turn to **299**.

455

Deduct 1 *STAMINA* point. Do you have a vial of glue? If not, turn to **13**. If you have a vial of glue, you may throw it at the Murderer and cast your spell on it. The vial will break and cover your opponent and your spell will set it solid, sticking his hands to the bow and his feet to the floor. You may leave through the door. Turn to **46**.

456

Deduct 2 *STAMINA* points. You cast the spell and wait for an indication of what will be the safest course of action. A feeling from within tells you that, although the fish has a nasty bite, it is nothing to be afraid of; there is no real danger here. You may put your head down to the fish (turn to **320**), try to snatch the Gold Piece (turn to **85**), or leave the pond (turn to **28**).

457

Deduct 1 *STAMINA* point. You may not choose this spell as you do not have the Jewel-Studded Medallion it requires. Return to **264** and choose again.

458

Deduct 1 *STAMINA* point. You cannot use this spell as you do not have the Stone Dust it requires. While you are trying to get it to work, the creatures move towards you. You will have to draw your weapon. Turn to **192**.

459

Deduct 1 *STAMINA* point. You cast your spell, but nothing happens. You cannot use this spell without the Pearl Ring it requires. As you try in vain, the Bristle Beast leaps at you with sharp jaws and bites your leg. Lose 3 *STAMINA* points and resolve the fight:

BRISTLE BEAST   *SKILL 5*   *STAMINA 7*

If you win, turn to **14**.

460

Deduct 5 *STAMINA* points. There is no such spell as this. Return to **234** and resolve the fight.

461

Deduct 4 *STAMINA* points. You cast this spell at the statue and will it to move. You have guessed correctly! It is indeed a living creature and, under your command, it steps towards you. You order it to hand you the locket from around its neck, then step back and resume its pose. It follows your instructions. Turn to **117**.

462

There is no such spell as this. Return to **290** and choose again. If you were not expecting this to be a spell, turn to **397**.

463

Deduct 1 *STAMINA* point. Do you have a Black Facemask with you? If not, your spell will not work – you must draw your weapon and turn to **192**. If you have such a Facemask, you may hold it to your face and cast the spell. The creatures watching you suddenly cower in terror from you! They throw back any Gold they have stolen and back away, allowing you to continue. Turn to **89**.

464

Deduct 4 *STAMINA* points. You cast your spell at the wooden wall and your companion hides his face as a bolt of lightning shoots from your fingertips and blasts the wood. Daylight appears through the hole in the boat's hull you have made and you breathe a sigh of relief – your aim has been above the water line. You can hear a commotion above on the deck, but before you can be recaptured, you climb through the hole on to the dockside. Turn to **487**.

465

Deduct 1 *STAMINA* point. You cannot use this spell as you do not have the Galehorn it requires. Return to **26** and make another choice.

466

Deduct 1 *STAMINA* point. You cannot use this spell as you do not have the ring of Green Metal it requires. Return to **47** and choose again.

467

Deduct 1 *STAMINA* point. This spell will not work as you do not have the Ring of Green Metal it requires. Return to **108** and make another choice.

468

Do you now want to:

Look for treasures worth stealing?	Turn to **205**
Investigate the idol?	Turn to **122**
Have a quick look round for traps?	Turn to **224**
Make sure no one is about?	Turn to **168**

469

Deduct 1 *STAMINA* point. Do you have a Bracelet of Bone? If not, this spell will not work – return to **234** and resolve the fight. If you have a Bracelet of Bone, you may put it on your wrist and cast the spell. You create the illusion that your favoured contestant has fallen over. The other fighter rushes over to take advantage and your fighter, since he has *not* really fallen over, may effect a quick attack. Deduct 2 *STAMINA* points from your fighter's opponent. But once this has happened, the illusion is broken and the fight will continue as normal. Return to **234** and resolve the fight.

470

Deduct 2 *STAMINA* points. You cast your spell and wait for any indication that magic may be involved. Nothing happens. There is no magic in the area. Return to **213** and choose your next move.

471

Do you have any Goblin teeth with you? If not, you cannot use this spell – deduct 1 *STAMINA* point and return to **77** to fight the Slime Eater with your weapon. If you have any Goblin teeth, throw as many as you wish in front of the Slime Eater and cast your spell on them. Deduct 1 *STAMINA* point for each tooth you use and turn to **505**.

472

Deduct 2 *STAMINA* points. You cast the spell and focus on the hut, waiting for a reaction to tell you whether a trap is imminent. The hut seems to be harmless. If you wish to enter, turn to **27**. The statue sets an alarm bell ringing in your mind, thanks to the spell. If you wish to investigate, turn to **8**. Otherwise you may leave (turn to **137**).

473

Deduct 2 *STAMINA* points. You cast your spell in the air at the HARPIES, but as they dart about, you cannot be sure that your aim will be accurate. You may, if you wish, *Test your Luck*. If you are Lucky, the spell will hit one of the creatures, confusing it so much that it will be no threat (toss a coin to see which Harpy is affected). If you are Unlucky, or if you do not wish to use your *LUCK*, the spell misses. Turn to **118** and fight the Harpies.

474

Deduct 4 *STAMINA* points. You hold up your hands and two glowing fireballs form in the palms. You hurl these at the lock of the door. The scorching heat begins to burn the door and you hide away from the doorway – the fire will certainly attract attention. Sure enough, two guards appear, jabbering in a strange language, and try unsuccessfully to put out the fire. They run off for water, leaving you free to dart inside. Inside, you dash immediately for cover.

There is a stone building with barred windows just inside the gate and you nip over to it. Looking in through the window, you can see it is bare inside except for a wooden bench on which an old man sits. Do you wish to enter the hut and greet the man (turn to **169**) or leave and continue onwards (turn to **218**)?

475

Deduct 2 *STAMINA* points. You promise the guards something more valuable than a few Gold Pieces. Reaching into your backpack, you cast the spell silently on something inside (you choose what – but whatever it is will be lost to you). You pull out a handful of false treasure and their eyes widen. You offer them all this if they will allow you through to the gate. They agree and greedily snatch the treasure from you, dividing it up and stuffing it into their pockets. You are allowed through to the North Gate. Turn to **271**. But you had better be quick, as the guards will soon discover the treasure to be worthless!

WIN 5 GOLD PIECES

476

Deduct 4 *STAMINA* points. You cast the spell and an invisible force-field forms around you. This force-field will protect you *on your next choice of reference only* (after this it will disappear). Do you now wish to rush into the room (turn to **249**) or reach into your backpack for something that may be useful (turn to **7**)?

477

Deduct 1 *STAMINA* point. Do you have a skullcap with you? If not, the spell will not work – turn to **468**. If you have a skullcap, you may place it on your head and cast the spell. If anything intelligent is around, you will be able to read its mind. But you receive no telepathic signals; there is probably no one about. Turn to **468**.

478

Deduct 5 *STAMINA* points. There is no such spell as this. You must now leave the hut and continue on your way. Turn to **137**.

479

Deduct 1 *STAMINA* point. Do you have a Green-Haired Wig with you? If not, you cannot use this spell and you will have to return to **77**, draw your weapon, and fight the monster. If you have a Green-Haired Wig, you may place it on your head and try to talk to the Slime Eater. You speak, and your voice comes out as a series of howls and roars. The language of the Slime Eater seems to be restricted to a small number of basic messages. It stops and listens to you, but then lurches forwards to attack. Fight the Slime Eater with your weapon:

SLIME EATER   *SKILL* 7   *STAMINA 11*

If you win, turn to **196**.

480

Deduct 1 *STAMINA* point. You cannot use this spell as you do not have the Potion of Fire Water it requires. While you are trying to cast it, one of the HARPIES drops from the sky and slashes your arm with its talons. Deduct 2 *STAMINA* points and turn to **118** to fight them.

481

Deduct 2 *STAMINA* points. You cast your spell and wait for an indication of a way out of this chain net. The spell is working, but there is no easy way out of your predicament. Turn to **154**.

482

Deduct 2 *STAMINA* points. You cast the spell and wait for the warning if magic is involved here. There are no warnings. You are safe to assume nothing magical will happen. Return to **153** and make another choice.

483

Deduct 1 *STAMINA* point. Do you have a Green-Haired Wig? If not, you may not cast this spell – return to **26** and choose again. If you have a Green-Haired Wig, you may place it on your head and cast the spell. As you speak to the guards, your words come out in a strange tongue. The guards are startled! They chatter to each other and turn towards you. 'Stranger you speak in Crolian, our own native tongue. Are you from Mauristatia?' You tell them you are and in the short conversation that follows, you persuade them to let you through to the North Gate. Turn to **271**.

484

Deduct 4 *STAMINA* points. You cast your spell and wait as a magical force-field forms around your body. Unfortunately, this is of little help to you as your problem is the fast-acting poison! The pain in your stomach is becoming acute and you are faced with certain death unless you are able to call on your goddess. Turn to **129** if you are able; otherwise your journey ends here.

485

Deduct 1 *STAMINA* point. Do you have any Blimberry juice or medicinal potions? If not, you cannot use this spell (turn to **468**). If so, you may drink this liquid and cast your spell. Your strength builds up rapidly and your wounds heal. You may restore your *STAMINA* to its *Initial* value. Then turn to **468**. Remember that you have used your potion.

486

Deduct 1 *STAMINA* point. You cast your spell but nothing happens. You cannot use it as you do not have the Staff of Oak Sapling it requires. Return to **254** and choose again.

487

From the ship you arrive on the near bank of the Jabaji in the docks area. Did you eat at all yesterday? If not, you must deduct 3 *STAMINA* points as you are now very hungry. You cross over the Jabaji on the Harbour Bridge ahead of you and on the far bank the road forks to give you two options onwards. Will you take the right fork (turn to **198**) or the left fork (turn to **132**)?

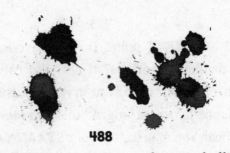

488

Deduct 1 *STAMINA* point. Do you have a skullcap with you? If not, the spell will not work. If so, you may place it oh your head and wait for telepathic messages from the slimy creature. Nothing happens. Probably the creature's brain is not capable of intelligent thoughts. But one thing is certain: it is out to attack you and while you have been conjuring up your spell, it has closed in. Draw your weapon and resolve this fight:

SLIME EATER   SKILL 7   STAMINA 11

If you win, turn to **196**.

489

Deduct 1 *STAMINA* point. Do you have a Bamboo Flute with you? If not, you may not use this spell and you will have to return to **24** and choose an escape route quickly. If you have such a Flute, you may pull it from your pack, cast your spell and play the instrument. Your pursuers stop. As if controlled by an invisible puppet-master, they begin to skip and hop uncontrollably in the street. You may use this opportunity to avoid them and continue your journey. Turn to **89**.

490

Deduct 2 *STAMINA* points. You drop your backpack on the ground and turn away from the Gnome. Reaching inside it, you cast your spell and turn one of the articles you have inside your pack into an illusionary pile of treasure. You may choose which article you will use (if you have nothing, you may choose some Provisions or, failing that, you will not be able to create any treasure). You hold out your offering, telling him you want to be able to choose two of his items for this treasure. He considers the deal – and accepts. Return to **264** and choose your two artefacts.

491

Deduct 4 *STAMINA* points. You cast your spell at the Statue and command it to return to its position. With fingers crossed, you wait for it to step backwards. It ignores your spell and swings forward trying to catch you in its hand. You leap out of the way in the nick of time and grab your weapon. Turn to **299**.

492

Deduct 2 *STAMINA* points. You cast your spell and wait for 'inner advice' on the best way to avoid any danger that may be threatening. As the spell takes effect, you feel the urge to run from this place. Will you follow this advice (turn to **55**) or draw your weapon (turn to **76**)?

493

Deduct 4 *STAMINA* points. You cast your spell and command the man to lay down his weapon. The Murderer merely laughs – this spell will work only on non-intelligent creatures! Turn to **13**.

494

Deduct 1 *STAMINA* point. You cast the spell but nothing happens. You cannot use this spell as you do not have the Potion of Fire Water it requires. Return to **235** and choose again.

495

Deduct 1 *STAMINA* point. Do you have a skullcap with you? If not, the spell will not work and, while you are trying to make it work, they surround you – turn to **330**. If you have a skullcap, you may place it on your head and cast your spell. You begin to pick up thoughts from the creatures and learn that they are RED-EYES. Although fairly normal with closed eyes, they are deadly if they open their eyes. Meanwhile, they are advancing and you will have to defend yourself with your weapon. Turn to **192**.

496

Deduct 2 *STAMINA* points. You cast the spell and immediately begin to grow in size and power. You step up to the closed South Gate and try to open it. You heave against the door, but cannot budge it. Eventually, you return to normal size, but your efforts have attracted attention within. Turn to **178**.

497

Deduct 2 *STAMINA* points. Do you have a Black Facemask with you? If not, this spell will not work. If you have a Black Facemask, you may pull it from your pack and cast the spell on it. But as you do so, the ruffian comes over. The crowd is booing you, since using magic in the fight is not allowed in the rules. The ruffian is terrified of you, but he will not let the fight commence if you are aided by magic. You will have to remove the mask. Turn to **323** and conduct your battle.

498

Deduct 1 *STAMINA* point. Do you have a skullcap with you? If not, you look pretty foolish, trying in vain to cast the spell; you had better drink the ale as he suggests – turn to **236**. If you do have a skullcap, turn to **444**.

499

Deduct 1 *STAMINA* point. Do you have any medicinal potions or Blimberry juice with you? If not, your spell will not work. If so, you may drink the liquid and cast your spell to regain your strength and restore your *STAMINA* to its *Initial* level. Now you may either enter the crypt (turn to **249**) or first pull something from your backpack (turn to **7**).

500

Deduct 1 *STAMINA* point. Do you have a Black Facemask? If not, your spell will not work and while you try to make something happen, the creature leaps on you and bites your ankle (lose 2 *STAMINA* points) – you must return to **95** and either fight or choose another spell. If you have the Facemask, you hold it in front of your face and cast the spell. The Bristle Beast shrieks in fear and its bristles stand on end! It faints with fright. Turn to **14**.

501

Deduct 1 *STAMINA* point. Do you have a Green-Haired Wig with you? If not, this spell will not work. If you have a Green-Haired Wig, you may place it on your head and cast your spell. The other bodies in the hold are stirring and your spell will now allow you to talk to them in their own languages. But none of them can come up with a decent plan of escape. Turn to **179**.

502

Deduct 2 *STAMINA* points. You cast the spell at the Chainmaker. His attack stops and he stares at you. You step forwards but his reactions are lethargic. His will to win has gone. Return to **119** and fight the Chainmaker. For the fight you may reduce his *SKILL* to 5 as a result of this spell.

503

Deduct 2 *STAMINA* points. You cast your spell and, in your mind's eye, a warning flashes. Before the altar is a dark circle woven into the carpet. You must avoid this. Turn to **468**.

504

Deduct 1 *STAMINA* point. Have you picked up any small pebbles on your journey? If not, you may not use this spell (return to **254** and choose again). If you have any pebbles, you may cast your spell on them and fling them at the bars on the window. They will explode on impact and destroy the bars. Three pebbles will be sufficient to let you and the old man escape (cross three pebbles off your Equipment List). You may both climb through the window and head on down the road towards Kharé. The old man is a brisk walker and soon leaves you behind. You arrive at a junction ahead. Turn to **81**.

505

As many Goblins appear as the teeth you used and you command them to attack the Slime Eater. But standing in water up to their waists, they are no match for the creature, who defeats them easily and turns to you. Draw your weapon and fight the monster:

SLIME EATER　　　　　　*SKILL 7*　　　*STAMINA 11*

If you win, turn to **196**.

506

Deduct 2 *STAMINA* points. You cast your spell and five extra images of you appear in front of the Orclings, forcing them to stop. If you had six or less items stolen, you have now recovered them. If you had more than six items stolen, you can only recover a maximum of six (you choose). Then you may continue. Turn to **61**.

507

Deduct 4 *STAMINA* points. You may cast this spell to make either of the fighters clumsy and uncoordinated. While under the effects of this spell, a fighter may only roll *one* die (instead of two) to find its Attack Strength. This effect will last for 6 Attack Rounds. But as you are casting this spell from a distance and there are two contestants close together, there is a chance that you may cast it on to the wrong fighter or even both! Nominate the fighter that you wish to cast the spell at and then roll one die. If you roll a 1,2 or 3 your aim is accurate. If you roll a 4 or 5, the spell hits the wrong person. If you roll a 6 the spell affects *both* fighters! Now return to **234** and resolve the battle.

508

Deduct 1 *STAMINA* point. You cast the spell at your advancing opponent, but nothing happens! You cannot use this spell as you do not have the Jewel-Studded Medallion it requires. While you are trying to make it work, your opponent lands a first blow. Lose 2 *STAMINA* points and continue the fight with your weapon. Remember your opponent has the same *SKILL* and *STAMINA* as you had before casting the spell and being struck. If you win, you may leave the hut. Turn to **137**.

509

Deduct 5 *STAMINA* points. You cannot cast this spell as it does not exist! Turn to **13**.

510

Deduct 1 *STAMINA* point. You may not use this spell as you do not have the Pearl Ring it requires. As you try to make it work without success, your pursuers close and you will have to draw your weapon. Turn to **192**.

Slowly the gate opens in front of you

511

Slowly the gate opens in front of you. You have overcome the dangers of the deadly city port and your journey is half over. Through the gate you can see the vast expanse of the Baklands laid before you. The great plains of Baddu-Bak are the next stage of your mission and your experience so far will be invaluable in guiding you through to Lake Ilklala.

You remember the words of the Sightmaster Sergeant as you left the Outpost Settlement: 'From Kharé you must cross the Baklands, which are unknown. It is said that day and night in the Baklands are controlled not by the sun but by supernatural forces ... from Kharé onwards your progress will be *watched*.'

The chinking of armour behind you snaps you out of your thoughts; the guards must be returning. Casting a final glance back at the city, you step through the gate. Ahead of you, dark clouds are heavy in the sky. You are now in the Baklands ...

HOW TO FIGHT THE CREATURES OF KHARÉ

Before setting off on your journey, you must first build up your own personality profile. On pages 296 and 298 you will find an *Adventure Sheet*. This is a sort of 'current status report' which will help you keep track of your adventure. Your own *SKILL, STAMINA* and *LUCK* scores will be recorded here, and also the equipment, artefacts and treasures you will find on your journey. Since the details will change constantly, you are advised to take photocopies of the blank *Adventure Sheet* to use in future adventures, or write in pencil so that the previous adventure can be erased when you start another.

SKILL, STAMINA AND LUCK

To determine your *Initial SKILL, STAMINA* and *LUCK* scores:

• Roll one die. If you are playing as a *warrior* (the simple game), add 6 to this number and enter this total in the *SKILL* box on the *Adventure Sheet*. If you are playing as a *wizard* (the advanced game), add only 4 to this number and enter the total. Wizards are worse fighters than warriors, but they more than make up for this by the use of magic spells.

• Roll both dice. Add 12 to the number rolled and enter this total in the *STAMINA* box.

• Roll one die, add 6 to this number and enter this total in the *LUCK* box.

For reasons that will be explained below, *SKILL*, *STAMINA* and *LUCK* scores change constantly during an adventure. You must keep an accurate record of these scores and for this reason you are advised either to write small in the boxes or to keep an eraser handy. But never rub out your *Initial* scores. Although you may be awarded additional *SKILL*, *STAMINA* and *LUCK* points, these totals may never exceed your *Initial* scores, except on very rare occasions, when you will be instructed on a particular page.

Your *SKILL* score reflects your swordsmanship and general fighting expertise; the higher the better. Your *STAMINA* score reflects your general constitution, your will to survive, your determination and overall fitness; the higher your *STAMINA* score, the longer you will be able to survive. Your *LUCK* score indicates how naturally lucky a person you are. Luck – and magic – are facts of life in the fantasy world you are about to explore.

BATTLES

When you are told to fight a creature, you must resolve the battle as described below. First record the creature's *SKILL* and *STAMINA* scores (as given on the page) in an empty Monster Encounter Box on your *Adventure Sheet*. The sequence of combat is then:

1. Roll the two dice for the creature. Add its *SKILL* score. This total is its Attack Strength.
2. Roll the two dice for yourself. Add your current *SKILL*. This total is your Attack Strength.
3. Whose Attack Strength is higher? If your Attack Strength is higher, you have wounded the creature. If the creature's Attack Strength is higher, it has wounded you. (If both are the same, you have both missed – start the next Attack Round from step 1 above.)
4. If you wounded the creature, subtract 2 points from its *STAMINA* score. You may use *LUCK* here to do additional damage (see 'Using Luck in Battles' below).
5. If the creature wounded you, subtract 2 points from your *STAMINA* score. You may use *LUCK* to minimize the damage (see below).
6. Make the appropriate changes to either the creature's or your own *STAMINA* scores (and your *LUCK* score if you used *LUCK*) and begin the next Attack Round (repeat steps 1–6).

7. This continues until the *STAMINA* score of either you or the creature you are fighting has been reduced to zero (death).

FIGHTING MORE THAN ONE CREATURE

If you come across more than one creature in a particular encounter, the instructions on that page will tell you how to handle the battle. Sometimes you will treat them as a single monster; sometimes you will fight each one in turn.

LUCK

At various times during your adventure, either in battles or when you come across situations in which you could be either lucky or unlucky (details of these are given on the pages themselves), you may call on your *LUCK* to make the outcome more favourable. But beware! Using *LUCK* is a risky business and if you are *un*lucky, the results could be disastrous.

The procedure for using your *LUCK* is as follows: roll two dice. If the number rolled is *equal to or less than* your current *LUCK* score, you have been *Lucky* and the result will go in your favour. If the number rolled is *higher* than your current *LUCK* score, you have been *Unlucky* and you will be penalized.

This procedure is known as *Testing your Luck*. Each time you *Test your Luck*, you must subtract one point from your current *LUCK* score. Thus you will soon realize that the more you rely on your *LUCK*, the more risky this will become.

USING LUCK IN BATTLES

On certain pages of the book you will be told to *Test your Luck* and will be told the consequences of your being *Lucky* or *Unlucky*. However, in battles you always have the *option* of using your *LUCK* either to inflict a more serious wound on a creature you have just wounded, or to minimize the effects of a wound the creature has just inflicted on you.

If you have just wounded the creature, you may *Test your Luck* as described above. If you are *Lucky*, you have inflicted a severe wound and may subtract an *extra* 2 points from the creature's *STAMINA* score. However, if you are *Unlucky*, the wound was a mere graze and you must restore 1 point to the creature's *STAMINA* (i.e. instead of scoring the normal 2 points of damage, you have now scored only 1).

If the creature has just wounded you, you may *Test your Luck* to try to minimize the wound. If you are *Lucky*, you have managed to avoid the full damage of the blow. Restore 1 point of *STAMINA* (i.e. instead of doing 2 points of damage it has done only 1). If you are *Unlucky,* you have taken a more serious blow. Subtract 1 *extra STAMINA* point.

Remember that you must subtract 1 point from your own *LUCK* score each time you *Test your Luck.*

RESTORING SKILL, STAMINA AND LUCK

SKILL

Your *SKILL* score will not change much during your adventure. Occasionally, you may be given instructions to increase or decrease your *SKILL* score. A Magic Weapon may increase your *SKILL* but remember that only one weapon can be used at a time! You cannot claim 2 *SKILL* bonuses for carrying two Magic Swords. Your *SKILL* score can never exceed its *Initial* value unless specifically instructed.

STAMINA AND PROVISIONS

Your *STAMINA* score will change a lot during your adventure as you fight monsters and undertake arduous tasks. As you near your goal, your *STAMINA* level may be dangerously low and battles may be particularly risky, so be careful!

If *Kharé* is your first adventure, you start with enough Provisions for two meals. If the have played *The Shamutanti Hills*, the amount of Provisions you carry will already have been decided. You may eat only one meal at a time. When you eat a meal, add points to your *STAMINA* score as instructed. Remember that you have a long way to go, so manage your Provisions wisely!

Remember also that your *STAMINA* score may never exceed its *Initial* value unless specifically instructed.

LUCK

Additions to your *LUCK* score are awarded through the adventure when you have been particularly lucky. Details are given whenever this occurs. Remember that, as with *SKILL* and *STAMINA,* your *LUCK* score may never exceed its *Initial* value unless specifically instructed.

SKILL, STAMINA and *LUCK* scores can be restored to their *Initial* values by calling on your goddess (see later).

WIZARDS: HOW TO USE MAGIC

If you have chosen to become a wizard you will have the option, throughout the adventure, of using magic spells.

All the spells known to the sorcerers of Analand, and rules for using them, are given in *The Sorcery! Spell Book,* and you will need to study this before you set off on your adventure.

All spells are coded with a three-letter code and you must learn and practise your spells until you are able to identify a reasonable number of them from their codes. Casting a spell drains your *STAMINA* and each has a cost, in *STAMINA* points, for its use. Recommended basic spells will get you started quickly, but are very uneconomical; an experienced wizard will use these only if faced with choices of unknown spells or if he/she has not found the artefact required for a less costly spell.

Full rules for using spells are given in the *Spell Book.*

LIBRA – THE GODDESS OF JUSTICE

During your adventure you will be watched over by your own goddess, Libra. If the going gets tough, you may call on her for aid. *But she will only help you once in each adventure.* Once you have called on her help in Kharé she will not listen to you again until you reach The Baklands.

There are three ways in which she may help you:

- *Revitalization:* You may call on her at any time to restore your *SKILL, STAMINA* and *LUCK* scores to their *Initial* values. This is not given as an option in the text; you may do this if and when you wish, but only once in each adventure.
- *Escape:* Occasionally, when you are in danger, the text will offer you the option of calling on Libra to help you.
- *Removal of Curses and Diseases:* She will remove any curses or diseases you may pick up on your adventure. This is not given as an option in the text; you may do this if and when you wish, but only once in each adventure.

EQUIPMENT AND PROVISIONS

You start your adventure with the bare necessities of life. You have a sword as your weapon, and a backpack to hold your equipment, treasures, artefacts and provisions. You cannot take your Spell Book with you, as the sorcerers of Analand cannot risk its falling into the wrong hands in Kakhabad – so you may not refer to this book at all once you have started your journey.

If you have not been through The Shamutanti Hills, you have a pouch around your waist containing 20 Gold Pieces, the universal currency of all the known lands. If this is the second stage of your adventure, your quota of Gold Pieces will already have been decided. You will need money for food, shelter, purchases and bribery throughout your adventure. You will find it necessary to collect more gold as you progress on your way.

You are also carrying Provisions (food and drink). As you will find, food is an important commodity and you will have to be careful how you use it. Make sure you do not waste food: you cannot afford to run out of Provisions.

THE SORCERY! SPELL BOOK
RULES FOR USING MAGIC

THE SIX MOST USEFUL SPELLS

During your training you have been taught a number of spells and incantations which you can call upon to aid you on your quest. The full list of spells follows these instructions.

Spells are identified by a three-letter word. Throughout the book you will be given the option of using spells to overcome problems and opponents. *The spells will be identified only by these three-letter words, so it is important that you memorize at least some of the codes.*

Thus, before you can start using your powers of sorcery, you will need to spend some time memorizing spells, as would a real wizard learning the magic arts. Obviously, you will not be able to memorize all forty-eight spells at once, but the more you use the book, the more familiar you will become with the most useful spells.

Try starting by memorizing between six and ten spells (the best ones to start with are given below) and relying on your swordsmanship to fight some of the creatures you encounter. It is possible, with a little luck, to complete your quest with these spells, but your task will become easier when you are capable of using more spells.

Some spells also require the use of an artefact, such as a piece of jewellery or a magic ring. If you try to use a spell without possessing the correct artefact, you will be wasting your *STAMINA* as the spell will not work.

Each time you use a spell – whether it is successful or not – it will draw on your reserves of energy and concentration. A cost, in *STAMINA* points, is given for each spell. Each time you use a spell, you must deduct this cost from your *STAMINA* score.

You may study the Book of Spells for as long as you want before embarking on an adventure, *but once you have set off, you may never again refer to it and must rely purely on your memory until your adventure is over.* Nor may you write the spells down for easy reference. In a real situation where you may be surprised by a creature, you would not have time to start flicking through your Spell Book trying to work out the best spell to cast!

CODE	EFFECT	STAMINA COST
ZAP	Creates a lightning bolt which shoots from the fingertip	4
FOF	Creates a protective force-field	4
LAW	Enables creatures to be controlled	4
DUM	Makes creatures extremely clumsy	4
HOT	Creates a fireball which can be aimed at enemies	
WAL	Creates a magic wall to defend against physical objects	4

ZAP and HOT are strong attacking spells, FOF and WAL are good general-purpose defensive spells, whilst LAW and DUM will be useful if you get into a tricky situation.

Note that these spells will often be more powerful than you need in a given situation – they are not cheap in terms of *STAMINA* points – but they are good all-rounders. As you get to know more spells from the Spell Book, you will be able to choose more economical spells which will be equally as effective against certain perils.

Read through the list again, then cover up the 'Effect' column with your hand. How many can you remember?

When you can remember them by heart, you can begin your quest.

HINTS ON USING SPELLS

As you familiarize yourself with the spells in this Spell Book, your skill and abilities in the adventure will improve.

Learning the six basic spells will allow you to start playing with minimal delay. These spells will get you out of most difficulties, but they are expensive (in terms of *STAMINA* points) and you will often find it necessary to rely on your limited powers of swordsmanship, particularly with weaker creatures, in order to avoid running dangerously short of *STAMINA*.

Other spells are more economical but will be given less often as options, thus relying more on your memory and skill as a wizard. The most economical spells of all are those which require magical artefacts, which must be found on your adventure.

Remember that there are heavy penalties for guessing spells! If you choose a spell code which does not represent a spell, or if you choose a spell for which you do not have the required artefact, you will lose extra *STAMINA* points. In some cases, death will be your penalty!

Not all the spells are used in this adventure.

You will soon begin to make your own discoveries about the spells themselves. There is a certain logic to the way they are arranged, the options that are given and their codes. But these discoveries you must make for yourself. Experience will make you more skilful with magic. All this is part of the art of sorcery.

Spell Book

ZAP

An extremely powerful weapon, this spell creates a blast of lightning which shoots from the caster's hand, which must be pointed in the desired direction. It is effective against virtually all living creatures which have no magical defences. But it takes great strength and concentration to use.

Cost 4 STAMINA points

HOT

The caster may direct this spell with his hands in any direction desired. As it is cast, a burning fireball shoots from the hands towards its target. It will be effective against any creature, whether magical or not, unless that creature cannot be harmed by fire. The fireball so created causes severe burns on impact, but is extinguished soon after hitting its target.

Cost 4 STAMINA points

FOF

This powerful spell creates in front of the caster a magical and physical barrier which is capable of keeping out all physical intruders and most magical ones. Its creation takes excessive mental concentration but the resulting force-field is both extremely strong and under the control of the will of its creator, who can allow one-way penetration, or can position it as desired.

Cost 4 STAMINA points

WAL

The casting of this spell creates an invisible wall in front of the caster. This wall is impervious to all missiles, creatures, etc. It is a very useful defensive spell.

Cost 4 STAMINA points

LAW

Casting this spell at an attacking creature allows the caster to take control of the attacker's will. The attack will cease and the creature will immediately come under the control of the caster. However, this spell works only on non-intelligent creatures and lasts only for a short time.

Cost 4 STAMINA points

DUM

When cast at a creature holding an object of some sort (e.g. a weapon), this spell will make the creature clumsy and uncoordinated. It will drop the object, fumble to pick it up, drop it again – in short, the creature is unlikely to do the caster any harm with any objects while under the influence of this spell.

Cost 4 STAMINA points

BIG

When this spell is cast on the caster's own body, it will inflate the body to three times normal size. This increases the power of the caster and is especially useful against large opponents, but must be used with caution in confined spaces.

Cost 2 STAMINA points

WOK

A Coin of some sort is necessary for this spell. The caster places the Coin on the wrist and casts the spell onto it. The Coin becomes magically fixed on the wrist and acts as an invisible metal shield with an effective protection circle of just under a metre across. This will shield the user from all normal weapons. Afterwards, the Coin is no longer usable as a coin.

Cost 2 STAMINA points

DOP

This spell may be used to open any locked door. Casting the spell works directly on the lock tumblers and the door may be opened freely. If the door is bolted from the inside, the bolts will be undone. The spell will not work on doors sealed by magic.

Cost 2 STAMINA points

RAZ

To perform this spell, Beeswax is required. If you rub this on any **edged** weapon (sword, axe, dagger, etc.) and cast this spell, the blade will become razor-sharp and do double its normal damage. Thus if it normally inflicts 2 *STAMINA* points' worth of damage, it will now inflict 4.

Cost 1 STAMINA point

SUS

This spell may be cast when the caster suspects a trap of some kind. Once cast, it will indicate telepathically to the caster whether or not to beware of a trap and, if so, the best protection action. If you are caught in a trap, this spell may also be used to minimize its effects in certain cases.

Cost 2 STAMINA points

SIX

This spell is cast onto the caster's own body. Its effect is to create multiple images of the caster, all identical and all capable of casting spells and/or attacking, although each will perform identical actions as if reflected in a mirror. Most creatures faced with these replicas will be unable to tell which is the real one and will fight all six.

Cost 2 STAMINA points

JIG

When this spell is cast, the recipient gets the uncontrollable urge to dance. The caster can make any creature dance merry jigs by playing a small Bamboo Flute. If this Flute has been found, the affected creature will dance for as long as it is played. This will normally give the caster time to escape – or he may continue playing and watch the show!

Cost 1 STAMINA point

GOB

This creation spell requires any number of Goblins' Teeth. The spell may be cast onto these Teeth to create one, two, or an army of Goblins. These Goblins can then be commanded to fight an enemy or will perform any duties they are instructed to carry out. They will disappear as soon as their duties have been performed.

Cost 1 STAMINA point per Goblin created

YOB

Casting this spell requires a Giant's Tooth. When this spell is cast upon the Tooth correctly, a Giant, some four metres tall, will be created instantly. The caster has control over the Giant and may command him to fight an opponent, perform some feat of strength, etc. The Giant will disappear when his duty is done.

Cost 1 STAMINA point

GUM

Casting this spell, together with using the contents of a Vial of Glue, will cause the Glue to become super-sticky, bonding in less than a second. Using the spell, the caster will be able to stick creatures to the floor or walls, although it is necessary to get the victim into contact with the Glue from the Vial. This can be done, for instance, by throwing it at the creature's feet, or by resting it on top of a slightly opened door, so that it falls when the door is opened.

Cost 1 STAMINA point

HOW

This spell is to be used in perilous situations when information about the safest way of escape is desired. When it has been cast, the caster will get an inclination towards one exit or, if a means of defence is present near by, will be directed towards it by a strange psychic force.

Cost 2 STAMINA points

DOC

Medicinal Potions carried and used by the caster will, under this spell, have their effects increased so that they will heal any wounded human or creature who drinks them. The Potions may be used on the caster – the spell must be cast as the Potion is being administered – but they will not bring a being which has actually died back to life.

Cost 1 STAMINA point

DOZ

This spell may be cast upon any creature, reducing its movements and reactions to about a sixth of its normal speed. Thus the creature appears to move as in a dream sequence, making it much easier to evade or defeat.

Cost 2 STAMINA points

DUD

By casting this spell, the caster can create an illusion of treasure in its many forms. Gold pieces, silver coin, gems and jewels can be created at will and these can be used to distract, pay off or bribe creatures. The illusionary riches will disappear as soon as the caster is out of sight.

Cost 2 STAMINA points

MAG

This spell protects its caster from most magical spells. It must be cast quickly, before the attacking spell takes effect. It works by neutralizing the attacking spell which disperses harmlessly. This spell is thus a very powerful protective weapon, but it does not work against every spell.

Cost 2 STAMINA points

POP

A potent little spell, but one which calls for great mental concentration, this spell must be cast on Small Pebbles. Once charged with magic, these Pebbles can be thrown and will explode on impact. Apart from being dangerous to anything within shatter distance, the Pebbles make a loud bang when they explode.

Cost 1 STAMINA point

FAL

This spell is useful if the caster is caught in a pit trap or falls from a considerable height. When cast, it makes the caster's body as light as a feather. The caster will float down through the air and land gently on the ground.

Cost 2 STAMINA points

DIM

A good defensive spell, this can be cast at any creature attacking the caster. Its effect is to muddle the mind of its victim, temporarily confusing the creature. However, it must be handled with caution, as a creature so deranged may act irrationally and unpredictably.

Cost 2 STAMINA points

FOG

This spell may only be cast in a closed room with no windows. Once cast, the room turns pitch black in the eyes of all but the caster – even though torches and candles may still be burning. It renders blind any creatures within the room. Its effects are only temporary.

Cost 2 STAMINA points

MUD

As this spell is cast, the caster must sprinkle grains of Sand on to the floor as desired (e.g. in front of a creature). The spell takes effect on the Sand and the floor, creating a pool of quicksand. Any creature stepping on this quicksand will slowly be drowned in it.

Cost 1 STAMINA point

NIF

As this spell is cast, the air surrounding the caster becomes filled with a nauseating stench. This smell is so horrible that it will cause any creature which catches a whiff of it to vomit violently. It will thus weaken any adversary with a sense of smell. This includes the caster unless he is wearing a Pair of Nose Plugs. The effect will be more pronounced in creatures with large noses.

Cost 1 STAMINA point

TEL

To activate this spell, the caster must wear a Cloth Skullcap. With the aid of this Cap, the spell will allow the user to read the mind of any intelligent creature encountered, learning about its strengths, weaknesses, the contents of nearby rooms, etc.

Cost 1 STAMINA point

GAK

In order to use this spell, the caster must be in possession of a Black Facemask, which must be worn while the spell is being cast. It can be cast directly on to an opponent and has the effect of creating a terrible fear within his mind. Brave creatures will be less affected than cowardly ones, thus the effect varies from a cold sweat and loss of nerve to the creature's being reduced to a quivering jelly cowering in the corner of a room.

Cost 1 STAMINA point

SAP

The effect of this spell, which is only useful in combat, is to demoralize an opponent so that his will to win is lost. Any creature so demoralized will be easier to defeat – though victory is still not certain.

Cost 2 STAMINA points

GOD

This is a form of illusion spell which can only be performed if the caster is wearing a Jewel of Gold. When this spell is cast, any creatures or humans in the vicinity will take an immediate liking to the caster. This does not mean that they will not fight, if such is their duty, but they will be more likely to give information that they would not normally give. They may even help the caster in spite of their normally being hostile.

Cost 1 STAMINA point

KIN

This creation spell is useful in battles. It requires the use of a Gold-Backed Mirror, which must be pointed at a creature as the spell is cast. It creates an exact replica of any creature being fought and his double is under the control of the caster, who can instruct it to fight the original creature. Both will fight with the same strengths and weaknesses – only luck will separate their fates. If the original creature dies, its double will disappear. It will also disappear if it is defeated.

Cost 1 STAMINA point

PEP

A Potion of Fire Water must be taken by the caster for this spell to be used. It will enhance the effects of the Fire Water to give the caster double or treble his or her own normal strength. Although the effects are temporary, they will normally be enough to aid in battle or to perform some feat of super-strength.

Cost 1 STAMINA point

ROK

Special Stone Dust is required for this spell. The Dust must be thrown at a creature as the spell is being cast. Within seconds, the victim will start to petrify. As its movements become slower and eventually cease, it will start to turn grey. Some moments after the spell is cast, it will have solidified into a grey stone statue.

Cost 1 STAMINA point

NIP

The caster must cast this spell on his or her own body. Under the influence of this spell, the caster becomes exceedingly quick and may run, speak, think or fight at three times normal speed. However, this spell will only take effect if the caster sniffs Yellow Powder before using the spell.

Cost 1 STAMINA point

HUF

In order to use this spell, the caster must possess the Galehorn, a trumpet-like instrument which plays a discordant note. The spell is cast on to the Horn and it is blown in a particular direction. As the spell takes effect, a tremendous wind rushes from the Horn. This wind is capable of blowing over man-sized creatures, or it can be used to blow things off shelves, over ledges, etc.

Cost 1 STAMINA point

FIX

Applicable to both animate and inanimate objects, this spell has the effect of holding an opponent or object where it stands, unable to move even if in mid-air. In order to cast this spell, however, the caster must be holding a Staff of Oak Sapling. Anything held fast by this spell will remain frozen until the caster leaves the vicinity.

Cost 1 STAMINA point

NAP

Effective only against living creatures, this spell causes them to become drowsy and, within several seconds, to fall fast asleep. It is used in conjunction with a Brass Pendulum. The spell concentrates the creature's attention on the Pendulum, which the caster must swing slowly to and fro before the creature, in order to hypnotize it.

Cost 1 STAMINA point

ZEN

In order to cast this spell, the caster must wear a Jewel-Studded Medallion around the neck. Casting this spell will then allow the caster to float in the air at any height desired. A magician hovering thus will remain suspended for as long as desired and may float around at will.

Cost 1 STAMINA point

YAZ

This spell will not work unless the caster is wearing a fine Pearl Ring. Casting the spell while wearing this Ring renders the caster's body invisible to any reasonably intelligent creature. It may be used to give considerable advantage in battle or to escape from a dangerous situation. Any creature with ears will be able to hear the caster as he moves around the room. Less intelligent creatures will only be partially convinced, as this is a form of illusion spell.

Cost 1 STAMINA point

SUN

This spell may only be cast upon the yellow Sun Jewel. Once cast, the Jewel begins to glow brightly. Its intensity is under the control of the caster, who can make it brilliant – in order to blind attacking creatures – or just light enough to act as a torch to see in dark rooms.

Cost 1 STAMINA point

KID

In order to use this spell, the caster must be wearing a Bracelet of Bone. Once the spell is cast, the caster must concentrate on a particular illusion (e.g. the floor is made of hot coals, the caster has turned into a Demon, etc.) and this illusion will appear real in the eyes of its intended victim. This may allow time for escape or lower a creature's defences. The spell will not work on non-intelligent creatures. If the caster acts in such a way as to destroy the illusion (e.g. turns into a mouse and then goes on to strike the creature with a sword), its effect will be lost immediately.

Cost 1 STAMINA point

RAP

To use this spell, the caster must be wearing a Green-Haired Wig. In conjunction with this Wig, the spell will allow the caster to understand the language of, and communicate with, creatures speaking a non-human tongue (e.g. Goblins, Orcs, etc.).

Cost 1 STAMINA point

YAP

This spell allows the caster to understand the languages of, and communicate with, most animals. It will be ineffective unless the caster is wearing a Green-Haired Wig.

Cost 1 STAMINA point

ZIP

An invaluable aid in close battle, this spell is only usable when the caster is wearing a Ring of Green Metal, such Metal having been mined from the Craggen Rock. When the spell is cast on to his Ring, it enables the wearer to disappear, and reappear a short distance away. The transportation can be through some soft materials such as wood and clay, but is blocked by stone, metal and the like. It is a rather unreliable spell, though – occasionally it has disastrous results.

Cost 1 STAMINA point

FAR

In conjunction with an Orb of Crystal, this spell will enable its caster to see, with certain limitations, into the future. The Orb must be held in the hands and the spell is recited while concentrating on the Orb. Very little control can be exercised on exactly what will be seen, but the normal tendency is to see near-future events.

Cost 1 STAMINA point

RES

When cast upon a dead human or humanoid creature (i.e. one with two arms, two legs, a head, etc.) while Holy Water is being sprinkled on the corpse, this spell brings it back to life. The resurrection takes some time to work – the body does not simply spring back on its feet – and the ex-corpse can be killed again as normal. For some time after this spell has taken effect, the resurrected creature is dull and dozy, but it may answer questions asked of it by the caster.

Cost 1 STAMINA point

ZED

Casting this spell is beyond the means of most minor conjurers because of the great powers of concentration necessary. In fact, in all known history, this spell has been cast only once. Its caster, a powerful Necromancer from Throben, was never seen again and thus its effects are unknown. The Necromancer's notes were subsequently found, but only indications as to its effects could be assumed. Suffice it to say that this is perhaps the most formidable spell in known magic lore – but no living magician knows its true effect.

Cost 7 STAMINA points

ADVENTUIRE SHEET

SKILL	STAMINA	LUCK

EQUIPMENT & ARTIFACTS:

GOLD & TREASURE:

PROVISIONS:

BONUSES, PENALTIES, CURSES:

CLUES & NOTES

ENEMY ENCOUNTER SHEET

SKILL ☐ STAMINA ☐	SKILL ☐ STAMINA ☐	SKILL ☐ STAMINA ☐	SKILL ☐ STAMINA ☐
SKILL ☐ STAMINA ☐	SKILL ☐ STAMINA ☐	SKILL ☐ STAMINA ☐	SKILL ☐ STAMINA ☐
SKILL ☐ STAMINA ☐	SKILL ☐ STAMINA ☐	SKILL ☐ STAMINA ☐	SKILL ☐ STAMINA ☐
SKILL ☐ STAMINA ☐	SKILL ☐ STAMINA ☐	SKILL ☐ STAMINA ☐	SKILL ☐ STAMINA ☐
SKILL ☐ STAMINA ☐	SKILL ☐ STAMINA ☐	SKILL ☐ STAMINA ☐	SKILL ☐ STAMINA ☐
SKILL ☐ STAMINA ☐	SKILL ☐ STAMINA ☐	SKILL ☐ STAMINA ☐	SKILL ☐ STAMINA ☐

ADVENTURE SHEET

SKILL [ ]

STAMINA [ ]

LUCK [ ]

EQUIPMENT & ARTIFACTS:

GOLD & TREASURE:

PROVISIONS:

BONUSES, PENALTIES, CURSES:

CLUES & NOTES

ENEMY ENCOUNTER SHEET

| SKILL ☐ | SKILL ☐ | SKILL ☐ | SKILL ☐ |
| STAMINA ☐ | STAMINA ☐ | STAMINA ☐ | STAMINA ☐ |

| SKILL ☐ | SKILL ☐ | SKILL ☐ | SKILL ☐ |
| STAMINA ☐ | STAMINA ☐ | STAMINA ☐ | STAMINA ☐ |

| SKILL ☐ | SKILL ☐ | SKILL ☐ | SKILL ☐ |
| STAMINA ☐ | STAMINA ☐ | STAMINA ☐ | STAMINA ☐ |

| SKILL ☐ | SKILL ☐ | SKILL ☐ | SKILL ☐ |
| STAMINA ☐ | STAMINA ☐ | STAMINA ☐ | STAMINA ☐ |

| SKILL ☐ | SKILL ☐ | SKILL ☐ | SKILL ☐ |
| STAMINA ☐ | STAMINA ☐ | STAMINA ☐ | STAMINA ☐ |

| SKILL ☐ | SKILL ☐ | SKILL ☐ | SKILL ☐ |
| STAMINA ☐ | STAMINA ☐ | STAMINA ☐ | STAMINA ☐ |

YOU ARE THE HERO

FIGHTING FANTASY

SORCERY!
THE SHAMUTANTI HILLS

STEVE JACKSON

YOU, the hero, must search for the legendary Crown of Kings, and journey the Shamutanti Hills. Alive with evil creatures, lawless wanderers and bloodthirsty monsters, the land is riddled with tricks and traps waiting for YOU. Will YOU be able to cross the hills safely?

YOU ARE — THE HERO

FIGHTING FANTASY

CREATURE
— OF —
HAVOC

STEVE JACKSON

YOU, the hero, must find a way of defeating the feared necromancer Zharradan Marr. Access the Galleykeep, Marr's flying vessel, to destroy his portal and his means of entering Allansia – or perish in the attempt!

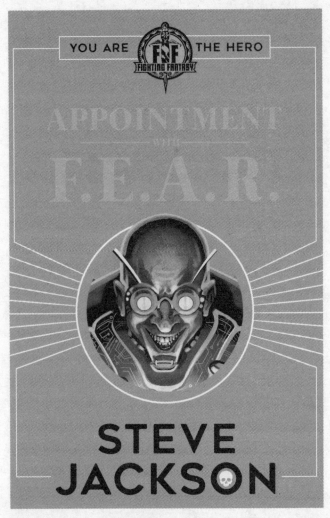

YOU ARE FnF FIGHTING FANTASY **THE HERO**

APPOINTMENT with F.E.A.R.

STEVE JACKSON☠

YOU are the Silver Crusader. YOU use your superpowers to discover the location of a top-secret F.E.A.R. meeting, capture the Titanium Cyborg and his gang, and bring them to justice and save Titan City. Can YOU complete this difficult quest?

ASSASSINS
—OF—
ALLANSIA

YOU ARE THE HERO
FIGHTING FANTASY

IAN LIVINGSTONE

After accepting a challenge to survive on Snake Island, a nightmare unfolds when a bounty is placed on your head. Beware the ruthless assassins hell bent on hunting you down – but who are they? Where are they? Trust no-one...

YOU ARE THE HERO

FIGHTING FANTASY

COLLECT THEM ALL, BRAVE ADVENTURER!

WARLOCK of FIRETOP MOUNTAIN

STEVE JACKSON
IAN LIVINGSTONE

CITY of THIEVES

IAN LIVINGSTONE

CITADEL of CHAOS

STEVE JACKSON

FOREST of DOOM

IAN LIVINGSTONE

HOUSE of HELL

STEVE JACKSO

THE PORT of PERIL

IAN LIVINGSTONE

DEATHTRAP DUNGEON

IAN LIVINGSTONE

CREATURE of HAVOC

STEVE JACKSON

ISLAND of the LIZARD KING

IAN LIVINGSTONE

STEVE JACKSO

SORCERY! SHAMUTANTI HILLS

STEVE JACKSON

GATES of DEATH

CHARLIE HIGSON

CAVERNS of the SNOW WITCH

IAN LIVINGSTONE

SORCERY! CITYPORT of TRAPS

STEVE JACKSON

ASSASSIN ALLANS

IAN LIVINGSTONE